# Maria Aylward

GILL EDUCATION

**Gill Education**
**Hume Avenue**
**Park West**
**Dublin 12**
www.gilleducation.ie

Gill Education is an imprint of M.H. Gill & Co.

© Maria Aylward 2017

**ISBN:** 978-0-7171-71767

**Editor:** Donna Garvin

**Design and layout:** Liz White Designs

**Illustrations:** Maria Murray

**Cover design:** Slickfish

**Cover illustration:** Derry Dillon

The authors and publisher have made every effort to trace all copyright holders. If, however, any have been inadvertently overlooked, we would be pleased to make the necessary arrangement at the first opportunity.

The paper used in this book is made from the wood pulp of managed forests. For every tree felled, at least one tree is planted, thereby renewing natural resources.

# Contents

# How to Use this Book

*Super Sleuth* is a unique mathematical problem-solving series for 1st to 6th Class primary school pupils. Problem-solving requires pupils to understand and explore a problem, find a strategy, use the strategy to solve the problem and look back and reflect on the solution. *Super Sleuth* focuses on the process of problem-solving and the development of the **ten main problem-solving strategies**. The series has **regular built-in revision** units, which consolidate problem-solving skills.

## Differentiation

Differentiation is catered for in each unit through the use of **bronze**, **silver** and **gold** medals that indicate the level of difficulty and provide an entry point for every pupil as well as opportunities for **high-achievers** to be challenged.

## Collaborative learning

**The series facilitates collaborative learning** through **whole-class**, **pair** and **group work** activities. This creates an ideal classroom environment for pupils to develop their maths language and thinking, in which the teacher can act as facilitator and every pupil's contribution is valued. Learning can be applied at home through practice.

## Dedicated strategy units

Each book dedicates **five units to a specific strategy** and pupils are encouraged to utilise and apply the strategies where relevant.

| Opportunity for pair work |
| :---: |
| **Duties** |
| Reader |
| Calculator |
| Checker |
| Reporter |
| Opportunity for group work |

## Super Sleuth's ten problem-solving strategies:

- Trial and improvement
- Working backwards
- Working systematically
- Logical reasoning
- Visualising/Draw a picture
- Identifying patterns
- Make a table
- Act it out
- Make a model
- Simplifying

## CLUES

CLUES is a teacher- and pupil-friendly **framework** developed uniquely for *Super Sleuth* to tackle the most common **problem-solving difficulties** experienced in the classroom. It was created in order to promote Bloom's higher forms of thinking in maths education.

---

Miss Carroll went to the art shop to buy a set of 28 small aprons and a set of 28 large aprons. How many aprons did she buy?

**C**ircle the numbers and keywords: 28, 28, how many?

**L**ink with operation needed (+ or −): Add (+).

**U**se a strategy: Draw a picture.

**E**stimate and calculate:

My estimate: more than 40

$$\begin{array}{r} \phantom{+}28 \\ +28 \\ \hline 56 \end{array}$$

**Answer:** 56

**S**ummarise how you got your answer: I added 2 groups of 28.

## Super Sleuth key features

**Weekly structure:** Weekly arrangement of work (30 units) and provides four days of work with three to four questions per day.

**WALT:** Clear learning outcomes are provided at the beginning of each new strand.

**Worked example:** A worked example using the CLUES framework is provided at the start of new strands to demonstrate a strategy that pupils can follow, allowing them to work independently.

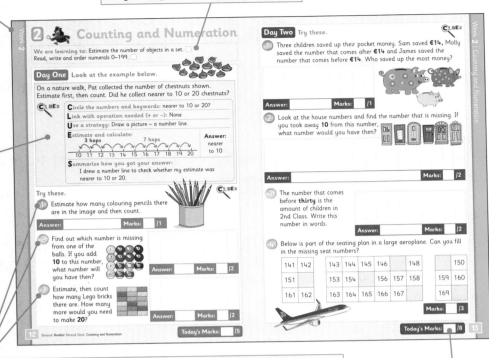

**Clear differentiation:** Each page is differentiated using bronze, silver and gold medals to show the level of difficulty and give pupils an incentive to progress. The bronze medal indicates a question that the majority of the class should work on independently. The silver medal poses more of a challenge, while the gold medal may require collaborative work in order for the pupils to reach a solution.

**Progress recording:** Each question and week has a score tracker to help pupils self-assess.

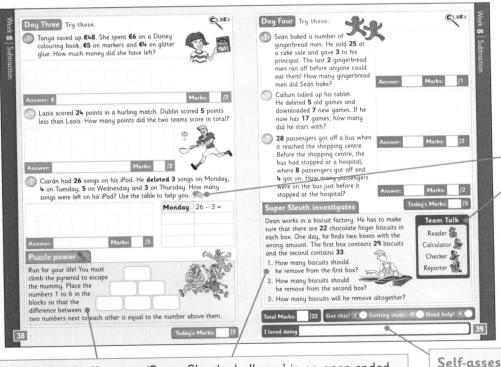

**Pair work/group work:** Opportunities are provided for pair and group work. Group work can be applied to activities and these specific questions are highlighted throughout the book, where different roles can be assigned to up to four pupils.

**Puzzles and challenges:** 'Super Sleuth challenge' is an open-ended question based on the maths skills and strand covered in the unit. 'Super Sleuth investigates' is an activity for applying the maths skills/strand of the unit to a situation that could be encountered in real life.

**Self-assessment:** The self-assessment section for each strand offers pupils an opportunity to reflect on their learning, as well as providing very valuable information to the teacher.

# Problem-solving strategies

## Trial and improvement

- The strategy of trial and improvement encourages pupils to make a reasonable estimate, giving them a starting point as they attempt to solve the puzzle.
- The pupils are then asked to check their estimate to see if it works as a solution and revise it accordingly.
- By repeating this process and changing their estimate appropriately, pupils should arrive at the correct answer.
- All rough work should be kept as a record of their work.

**Example:** On a farm there were some hens and cows. Altogether there were 8 heads and 22 feet. How many hens were there?

## Working backwards

- Occasionally pupils come across a puzzle in which they are given the final answer and the steps taken to arrive at the answer, but they are not given the data from the start of the puzzle. They must undo each step to get back to the starting point.
- Pupils can draw a diagram to show the known facts and use the inverse operation when working backwards.

**Example:** Martha removed a loaf of bread from the oven after it had been baking for two hours. If she took it out at 4 o'clock, at what time did she put it into the oven?

## Working systematically

- Working systematically requires pupils to work carefully through the information they are given.
- This strategy may incorporate other strategies for pupils to draw upon in order to work out the process of the problem. They might need to make a list, draw a diagram, make a table or explore problems with numerous answers in order to organise and build on the information until they find the solution.

**Example:** There are six ice-cream flavours to choose from. How many different two-scoop ice-cream cones can be made?

## Logical reasoning

- Logical reasoning can be explained as a proper or reasonable way of thinking about something. It requires the pupils to think carefully about the information they have been given and decide on a way of using the information to solve the puzzle.
- Pupils are encouraged to use a step-by-step approach to reach a solution.
- This may involve implementing a strategy such as visualisation or making a table.

**Example:** Grumpy, Sneezy, Sleepy and Doc are all in line for the cinema. Sleepy is ahead of Grumpy, Sneezy is behind Grumpy and Doc is second. What is their order from first to last?

## Visualising / Draw a picture

- Drawing a diagram can help pupils to visualise a puzzle. By doing this, they can make connections within the puzzle and plan how to solve it.
- Diagrams can include tree diagrams, timelines, pictures, symbols and Venn diagrams.

**Example:** Felix made 12 butterfly buns and iced them. He placed two chocolate buttons on top of each bun. How many chocolate buttons did he use?

## Identifying patterns

- This strategy involves pupils investigating how numbers, images or symbols are arranged in a variety of orders.
- Each pattern follows a rule. Pupils may be asked to identify the rule in a pattern, find the missing value(s) or extend the existing pattern. Many things in our world follow a set of rules, so that we know what to expect.

**Example:** Millie is making a beaded necklace that follows a pattern of red, green, blue. If she uses 18 beads in total, how many red beads will she use?

## Make a table

- When puzzles are written in word sentences, they can be confusing for pupils.
- Making a table helps pupils to organise the information that they have and identify the information that they need.

**Example:** Mikey saves €4 on Monday. Each day after that, he saves twice as much as the day before. How much money will he have saved by Friday?

## Act it out

- Acting it out is an effective strategy for pupils who have difficulty visualising a problem.
- Acting out a problem using props such as cubes or string, or in pairs or groups can greatly simplify finding solutions and is an effective strategy for demonstration purposes in front of the whole class.

**Example:** I have a 5 litre jug and a 3 litre jug. How can I measure out 7 litres of juice using these jugs?

## Make a model

- By making a model, the pupils are given an opportunity to showcase their understanding of a specific area of maths. For example, pupils can investigate the properties of 3-D shapes through model building.

**Example:** Using 26 cocktail sticks and Blu-tack, how many cubes can Emily make and how many cocktail sticks will be left over?

## Simplifying

There are three ways in which pupils can simplify a puzzle:

- Reword the puzzle using a more familiar setting.
- Break the puzzle down into steps and solve one part at a time.
- Use smaller numbers.

**Example:** Amy spent $\frac{1}{8}$ of her savings on a new jacket. If she had €320 in savings, how much did the jacket cost?

$\frac{1}{8}$ of €32 = €4 ➡ $\frac{1}{8}$ of €320 = €40

# 1 Strategy: Draw a Picture

## Day One

Sometimes when you read a number story, it might not be clear what you should do to solve it. Close your eyes and picture some of the things or people in the story and then draw them. Write the numbers near the things or people in your drawing. Your drawing might also be a diagram, a number line, a bar model or a table.

**Example:** Tony owns a farm. One day, he trims the hooves of 5 of his piglets. How many hooves does he trim altogether?

$$4 + 4 + 4 + 4 + 4 = 20$$

Today, we will draw a diagram to help us solve each number story.

**Try these.**

1. Kathia has three square play mats. She places **3** toys on each mat and then adds **1** more toy to two of the mats. How many toys does she use? Draw a diagram.

   Answer: _____ Marks: ___ /1

2. Martha had **8** jellies. She gave **half** to her friend Gina, who then gave **half** to her sister Tina. How many jellies did Tina get? Draw a diagram.

   Answer: _____ Marks: ___ /2

3. Mark made a **square** play fort in his sitting room. He used **3** chairs for each side and covered them with a blanket. How many chairs did he use? Draw a diagram.

   Answer: _____ Marks: ___ /2

Today's Marks: ___ /5

**Day Two** Try these.

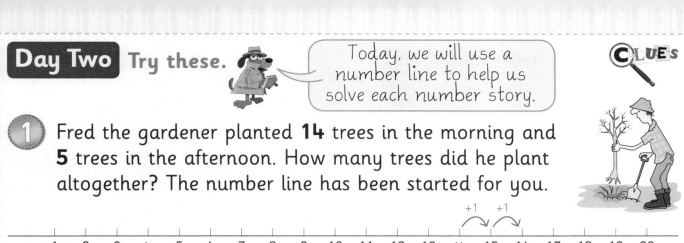

Today, we will use a number line to help us solve each number story.

**C**LUE**S**

**1** Fred the gardener planted **14** trees in the morning and **5** trees in the afternoon. How many trees did he plant altogether? The number line has been started for you.

+1  +1

1  2  3  4  5  6  7  8  9  10  11  12  13  14  15  16  17  18  19  20

Answer:                                    Marks:          /1

**2** Alison the art teacher put **6** water jars on one table, **7** on another table and **5** on another table. How many water jars were there altogether?

1  2  3  4  5  6  7  8  9  10  11  12  13  14  15  16  17  18  19  20

Answer:                                    Marks:          /1

**3** Every child wears flip-flops before they get into the swimming pool. If there are **16** individual flip-flops beside the pool, how many children are in the water? Use the number line above to help you.

Answer:          Marks:          /2

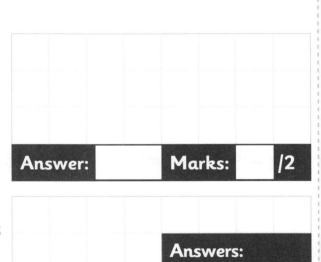

**4** Jamie is **7** years old. Lisa is **2** years **younger** than Jamie. Mark is **4** years **older** than Lisa. How old is **(a)** Lisa and **(b)** Mark? Use the number line above to help you.

Answers:

(a)          (b)

Marks:          /2

Today's Marks:          /6

**Day Three** Try these.

Today, we will use a bar model to help us visualise each number story.

**1** Charlotte has **2** braids in her hair, Della has **1**, Paula has **3** and Jade has **2**. How many braids are there altogether?

| ? | | | |
|---|---|---|---|
| 2 braids | 1 braid | 3 braids | 2 braids |

Answer: | Marks: | /1

**2** Evan has **16** cups. **3** have butterflies painted on them, **4** have leaves on them and the rest have roses on them. How many have roses?

**16 cups**

| 3 cups | 4 cups | ? |
|---|---|---|

Answer: | Marks: | /2

**3** At a superhero birthday party, **6** boys were dressed up as Spider-Man, **4** as Batman, **5** as Superman, **9** as the Incredible Hulk and the rest as Captain America. If there were **28** boys in total, how many were dressed up as Captain America?

**28 boys**

| 6 Spider-Man | 4 Batman | 5 Superman | 9 Incredible Hulk | ? |
|---|---|---|---|---|

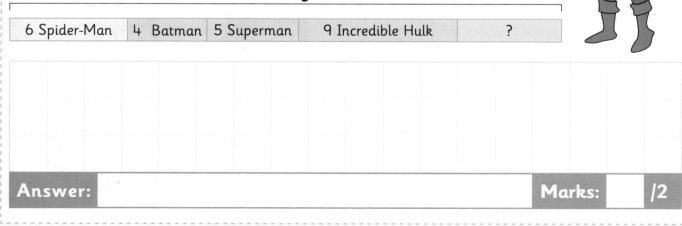

Answer: | Marks: | /2

10

Today's Marks: | /5

## Day Four   Try these.

Today, we will use a table to help us solve each number story.

 **CLUES**

**1** Harry built a tower with **6** blocks in the 1st row, **5** in the 2nd row, **4** in the 3rd row and so on. He continued using 1 less block in each row. How many blocks did he use in total? Fill in the table.

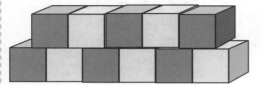

| 1st row | 2nd row | 3rd row | 4th row | 5th row | 6th row | Total |
|---|---|---|---|---|---|---|
| 6 | 5 | 4 | | | | |

Answer: _____   Marks: ____ /2

**2** Nick and Anna were in a baking competition. They each baked a pie and a cake.

- Nick got **7** marks for his pie and **18** marks for his cake.
- Anna got **17** marks for her pie and **6** marks for her cake.

Who got the highest score? Fill in the table.

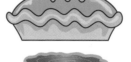

| | Nick | Anna |
|---|---|---|
| **Pie** | | |
| **Cake** | | |
| **Score** | | |

Answer: _____   Marks: ____ /2

**3** Ellie has **3 pairs** of earrings. Katie has **4 pairs** of earrings. How many **single** earrings do they have altogether? Fill in the table.

| | Pairs of earrings | Single earrings |
|---|---|---|
| **Ellie** | 3 | 6 |
| **Katie** | | |
| **Total** | | |

Answer: _____   Marks: ____ /2

Today's Marks: ____ /6

Total Marks: ____ /22   Got this!  ○   Getting there.  ○   Need help!  ○

I helped my friend by _____

**11**

# 2  Counting and Numeration

**We are learning to:** Estimate the number of objects in a set. ☐
Read, write and order numerals 0–199. ☐

## Day One  Look at the example below.

On a nature walk, Pat collected the number of chestnuts shown.
Estimate first, then count. Did he collect nearer to 10 or 20 chestnuts?

**C**lues

**C**ircle the numbers and keywords: nearer to 10 or 20?

**L**ink with operation needed (+ or –): None

**U**se a strategy: Draw a picture – a number line.

**E**stimate and calculate:

3 hops          7 hops

10  11  12  13  14  15  16  17  18  19  20

**Answer:**
nearer
to 10

**S**ummarise how you got your answer:
I drew a number line to check whether my estimate was
nearer to 10 or 20.

## Try these.

**1** Estimate how many colouring pencils there
are in the image and then count.

**C**lues

**Answer:** [        ]  **Marks:** [   ] /1

**2** Find out which number is missing
from one of the
balls. If you add
**10** to this number,
what number will
you have then?

1  2  3  4
5  6  7  8
9  10  11  12
13  14  15

**Answer:** [        ]  **Marks:** [   ] /2

**3** Estimate, then count
how many Lego bricks
there are. How many
more would you need
to make **20**?

**Answer:** [        ]  **Marks:** [   ] /2

Strand: Number Strand Unit: Counting and Numeration

**Today's Marks:** [        ] /5

**Day Two** Try these.

1 Three children saved up their pocket money. Sam saved **€14,** Molly saved the number that comes after **€14** and James saved the number that comes before **€14**. Who saved up the most money?

S    m    J
€14  €15  €13

**Answer:** molly    **Marks:** ⬜ /1

2 Look at the house numbers and find the number that is missing. If you took away **10** from this number, what number would you have then?

76  77  80  81
79

**Answer:** ⬜ **Marks:** ⬜ /2

3 The number that comes before **thirty** is the amount of children in 2nd Class. Write this number in words.

**Answer:** ⬜ **Marks:** ⬜ /2

4 Below is part of the seating plan in a large aeroplane. Can you fill in the missing seat numbers?

| 141 | 142 |
|-----|-----|
| 151 |     |
| 161 | 162 |

| 143 | 144 | 145 | 146 |     | 148 |
|-----|-----|-----|-----|-----|-----|
| 153 | 154 |     | 156 | 157 | 158 |
| 163 | 164 | 165 | 166 | 167 |     |

|     | 150 |
|-----|-----|
| 159 | 160 |
| 169 |     |

*Aer Lingus*

**Marks:** ⬜ /3

**Today's Marks:** ⬜ /8

## Day Three  Try these.

**1** A teacher had the dates for the last week in May all mixed up. Can you put the dates (numbers only) in the correct order?

| May 30 | May 26 | May 27 | May 25 | May 31 | May 29 | May 28 |

Answer: _____  Marks: ___ /1

**2** In Toys 4 U, Cathy is looking at boxes of toy cars. There are **10** cars in each box. Cathy can see a total of **7** boxes. How many toy cars are there altogether?

Answer: _____  Marks: ___ /1

**3** A post woman delivered **thirty-eight** parcels on Monday. **(a)** Using numbers or digits only, write down the number of parcels that she delivered. **(b)** How many more would you need to make **50**?

Answers: (a) _____  (b) _____  Marks: ___ /2

## Puzzle power

| | | 2 | 5 | 7 | 21 | 33 |
| | | 4 | 6 | 8 | 9 | 15 |
| 47 | 17 | 13 | 12 | 10 | 45 | 32 |
| 31 | 18 | 16 | 14 | 35 | 25 | 37 |
| 11 | 20 | 22 | 23 | 43 | 38 | 49 |
| 39 | 27 | 24 | 25 | 29 | | |
| 41 | 49 | 26 | 28 | 30 | | |

Can you help the monkey to find its way to the banana by counting in 2s? Colour the correct boxes to make a path.

Today's Marks: ___ /4

## Day Four Try these.

**1** Order the numbers on the marathon runners' bibs, starting with the **smallest** number.

| 73 | 26 | 124 | 11 | 108 | Marks: | /1 |

**2** Estimate how many water bottles there are in this image. Did you use any skip counting to help you?

Answer: _____ Marks: [ ] /2

**3** This is the number of houses in 1 estate. How many estates would be needed to build **40** houses?

Answer: _____ Marks: [ ] /2

Today's Marks: [ ] /5

## Super Sleuth investigates

1. Estimate the number of lollipops in the image.

2. Count the lollipops. How many are there?

3. Look at each row of lollipops. Can you work out which colour is missing a lollipop? How many should it have? (Hint: Look for a pattern.)

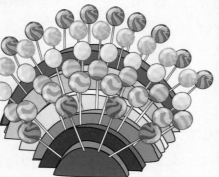

**Team Talk**

Reader

Calculator

Checker

Reporter

Total Marks: [ ] /22    Got this!  ◯  Getting there.  ◯  Need help!  ◯

I loved doing _____

15

# 3 Comparing and Ordering

**We are learning to:** Compare sets by using <, > or =. ☐ Order sets of objects by number. ☐ Use the language of ordinal number, first (1st) to tenth (10th). ☐

**Day One** Look at the example below.

Ben has €25 and Susan has €13. Who has more money using < or >?

**C**LUES

**C**ircle the numbers and keywords: €25, €13

**L**ink with operation needed (+ or −): None

**Top Tip!**

< means less than.
> means greater than.

**U**se a strategy: Act it out with money.

**E**stimate and calculate:
   €25 is greater than €13.    €25 > €13

**Answer:**
€25 > €13

**S**ummarise how you got your answer:
   I understood that €25 is more than €13.

**Try these.**

Use the symbols <, > or = in your answers below.

1. George has **10** tennis balls. Fiona has **14** tennis balls. Eva has **8** tennis balls. Who has the most tennis balls?

Answer: _____ Marks: ___ /1

2. Eric has **18** Match Attax stickers. Fionn has **9** fewer than Eric. Ciara has **6** more than Fionn. Who has the least stickers?

Answer: _____ Marks: ___ /2

3. Jill, Max and Hannah are playing a computer game. Jill has **8** points. Max has **3** points more than Jill. Hannah has **double 4** points. Which pair have the same number of points?

Answer: _____ Marks: ___ /2

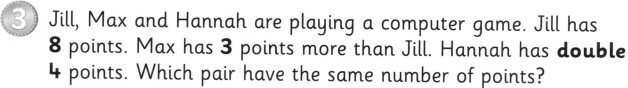

**Today's Marks:** ___ /5

## Day Two Try these.

Use the symbols <, > or = in your answers below.

**1** On their birthday cakes, Michael had **8** candles, Bernard had **2 more** than Michael, Trina had **1 less** than Michael and Simon had half of **20** candles. Which children are the same age?

**Answer:** | **Marks:** | /1

**2** Tanya has **14** computer games, Noel has **15** and Alex has **27**. **(a)** How many computer games do Tanya and Noel have altogether? **(b)** Is this **less than** (<) or **greater than** (>) Alex's number of games?

**Answers: (a)** | **(b)** | **Marks:** | /2

**3** Four horses ran a race. The **brown** horse did **not** come 1st or 2nd. The white horse came **after** the **brown** horse. The **black** horse came **after** the grey horse and before the **brown** horse. Order the horses by colour from 1st to 4th places.

**Top Tip!**
Use trial and improvement.

| 1st Place | 2nd Place | 3rd Place | 4th Place |
| --- | --- | --- | --- |
| | | | |

**Marks:** | /4

**Today's Marks:** | /7

## Day Three Try these.

**1** A school held a Readathon to see which class could read the greatest amount of books in a week. Miss Collins's class read **63** books. Miss Hickey's class read **86** books. Miss Breen's class read **79** books. Put the numbers of books in the correct order from 1st to 3rd places.

| 1st Place | 2nd Place | 3rd Place |
|---|---|---|
|  |  |  |

Marks: /1

**2** Grace got **twenty-six** raisins in her fruit bag. Shauna got **6 more** than Grace and Mark got **7 less** than Shauna. Who got the **least** amount? Use the symbols < or > in your answer.

Answer: 

Marks: /2

**3** There were **5** cars in a race. The **pink** car did **not** come 1st, 2nd or 3rd. The **blue** car came **after** the **red** car. The **green** car came **before** the **pink** car. The **grey** car came **before** the **green** car, but **after** the **blue** car. Order the cars by colour from 1st to 5th places.

**Top Tip!**
Use trial and improvement.

| 1st Place | 2nd Place | 3rd Place | 4th Place | 5th Place |
|---|---|---|---|---|
|  |  |  |  |  |

Marks: /3

Today's Marks: /6

**Day Four** **Try these.**

**C**LUE**s**

**1** The **red** bus has **52** seats, the **green** bus has **36**, the **purple** bus has **15** and the **yellow** bus has **25**. Put the buses in order from the largest to the smallest using 1st to 4th.

| | | | |
|---|---|---|---|
| | | | |

Marks: /1

**2** Yesterday morning, six **green** aeroplanes, three **yellow** aeroplanes, five **blue** aeroplanes and four **orange** aeroplanes landed at Dublin Airport. Was the total number of **green** and **blue** aeroplanes **greater than** or **less than** the total number of **yellow** and **orange** aeroplanes?

Answer: Marks: /2

**3** Write the birthdays of the six friends below in the order in which they come in the year. Write '**st**', '**nd**', '**rd**' or '**th**' after each date. The first one has been done for you.

- Sasha: September 21
- Greg: January 3
- Harry: May 14
- Shane: July 22
- Emma: October 31
- Orla: March 11

| Greg | January 3rd |
|---|---|
| | |
| | |
| | |
| | |
| | |

Marks: /3

Today's Marks: /6

Total Marks: /24    Got this! 👍○   Getting there. 👍○   Need help! 👎○

I would like to get better at

# 4 Place Value

**We are learning to:** Group and count in units, tens and hundreds. ☐ Rename numbers as hundreds, tens and units. ☐ Explore place value 0–199. ☐

## Day One — Look at the example below.

Deirdre has 28 daffodils and she wants to make groups of 10. How many groups of 10 can she make?

**C**ircle the numbers and keywords: 28 daffodils, groups of 10

**L**ink with operation needed (+ or –): None

**U**se a strategy: Draw a picture.

**E**stimate and calculate:

**Answer:**
2 groups of 10

**S**ummarise how you got your answer:
I drew 28 daffodils and a ring around each group of 10. There were 2 groups of 10 and 8 left over.

## Try these.

**CLUES**

1. Jordan is packing carrots into bags. He must pack **10** carrots into each bag. How many bags can he fill from **20** carrots?

Answer: [ ]     Marks: [ ] /1

2. Caoimhe has picked **30** daisies. How many groups of 10 can she make with them?

Answer: [ ]     Marks: [ ] /1

3. In PE, the teacher puts **35** children into groups of 10. **(a)** How many groups of 10 will there be? **(b)** How many children will not be in a group of 10?

Answers: (a) [ ]   (b) [ ]   Marks: [ ] /2

Today's Marks: [ ] /4

**Day Two** Try these.

CLUES

**1** Lisa spent **€23** at the shop. How many €2 and €1 coins might she have used to pay for her shopping? (There is more than one correct answer.)

**Top Tip!**
Act it out.

Answer: | Marks: | /2

**2** Nigel works in a clothes shop. He has to fold T-shirts and put them in bundles of 10. There are **54** T-shirts. How many bundles of 10 can he make?

**Top Tip!**
Use the hundred square to mark off each bundle of 10.

| 1 | 2 | 3 | 4 | 5 | 6 | 7 | 8 | 9 | 10 |
|---|---|---|---|---|---|---|---|---|---|
| 11 | 12 | 13 | 14 | 15 | 16 | 17 | 18 | 19 | 20 |
| 21 | 22 | 23 | 24 | 25 | 26 | 27 | 28 | 29 | 30 |
| 31 | 32 | 33 | 34 | 35 | 36 | 37 | 38 | 39 | 40 |
| 41 | 42 | 43 | 44 | 45 | 46 | 47 | 48 | 49 | 50 |
| 51 | 52 | 53 | 54 | 55 | 56 | 57 | 58 | 59 | 60 |
| 61 | 62 | 63 | 64 | 65 | 66 | 67 | 68 | 69 | 70 |
| 71 | 72 | 73 | 74 | 75 | 76 | 77 | 78 | 79 | 80 |
| 81 | 82 | 83 | 84 | 85 | 86 | 87 | 88 | 89 | 90 |
| 91 | 92 | 93 | 94 | 95 | 96 | 97 | 98 | 99 | 100 |

Answer: | Marks: | /1

**3** Zach is making up party bags. He wants to put 10 jellies into each bag. He has **76** jellies. **(a)** How many full bags can he make? **(b)** How many more jellies would he need to make another full bag?

Answers: (a) | (b) | Marks: | /2

**Super Sleuth investigates**

At a dog show, there are 45 poodles and 36 pugs. Each breed of dog goes into the parade ring in groups of 10.

**1.** How many groups of poodles go in and how many are left over?

**2.** How many groups of pugs go in and how many are left over?

**Day Three** Try these.

**1** A digit has fallen off the 3rd door in a row of houses. What is the value of the missing digit?

Answer: ☐ Marks: ☐ /1

**2** Maya and Sam are playing cards. They each have 3 cards. **(a)** By adding the numbers on Maya's cards together, how many even groups of 10 can she make? **(b)** Which card should Sam remove to make an even group of 10?

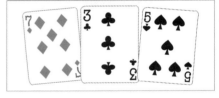

**Maya's cards**

**Sam's cards**

Answers: (a) ☐ (b) ☐ Marks: ☐ /2

**3** Bobby's teacher brought 127 seashells into school. What is the value of **(a)** the digit **1** and **(b)** the digit **7** in the number **127**?

Answers: (a) ☐ (b) ☐ Marks: ☐ /2

**Puzzle power** ✏️

From a box of 159 Lego bricks:

1. How many hundreds are there?
2. When you take away the hundreds, how many tens are left?
3. When you take away the tens, how many units are left?

**Team Talk**

Reader 🐶

Calculator 🐶

Checker 🐶

Reporter 🐶

Today's Marks: ☐ /5

**Day Four** Try these.

**1** In a sweet shop, there are **183** bonbons in a jar. The shopkeeper takes out one hundred bonbons. How many groups of ten are left in the jar? Record your answer on the abacus.

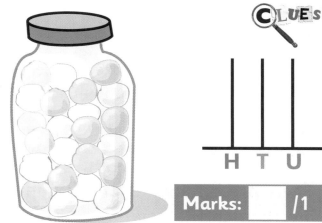

H T U

Marks: /1

**2** Nora won **€143** at bingo. **(a)** She spent the hundreds on a new coat. How many €100s was this? **(b)** She spent the tens on a pair of shoes. How many €10s was this? **(c)** She gave the units to her grandson. How many €1s was this? Record your answers on the abacus.

H T U

Marks: /3

**3** Martin has **one hundred and thirty-six** euro. Jill has o**ne hundred and seventy-four** euro. Fill in the table.

|  | €100s | €10s | €1s |
| --- | --- | --- | --- |
| Martin |  |  |  |
| Jill |  |  |  |

**Top Tip!**
Write the money in digits first.

Marks: /2

**4** Look at your table above. Write a number sentence to show whether Jill's amount is **greater than** or **less than** Martin's amount.

Answer: Marks: /1

Today's Marks: /7

Total Marks: /21 Got this!  Getting there.  Need help!

I enjoyed

# 5 🐕 Addition

**We are learning to:** Make number sentences for number stories that involve adding within 99. ☐ Add numbers within 99. ☐

## Day One  Look at the example below.

There are 8 bananas and 9 apples in a bowl. How many pieces of fruit are there in the bowl?

**C**LUEs 🔍

**Top Tip!**

Tips for adding 8 + 9:

8 + 8 = **16**
16 + 1 = **17**
**or**
8 + 10 = **18**
18 – 1 = **17**
or
9 + 9 = **18**
18 – 1 = **17**

**C**ircle the numbers and keywords: 8 bananas, 9 apples

**L**ink with operation needed (+ or –): Add (+).

**U**se a strategy: Draw a picture.

**E**stimate and calculate:

My estimate: less than 20

| T | U |
|---|---|
|   | 8 |
| + | 9 |
| 1 | 7 |

**Answer:**
17

**S**ummarise how you got your answer:
I added up all of the pieces of fruit.

## Try these.

**C**LUEs 🔍

**1** In a hurling match, Kevin scored **16** points and Austin scored **13** points. How many points did they score altogether?

Answer: ____
Marks: ____ /1

**2** A farmer has **29** sheep and **16** lambs. How many animals does she have altogether?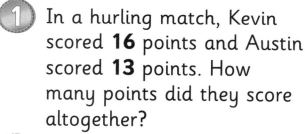

Answer: ____   Marks: ____ /1

**3** Amy has **4 packs** of stickers with **10** in each pack. She also has **5** loose stickers. Write a number sentence to work out how many stickers she has.

Answer: ____   Marks: ____ /2

Strand: Number Strand Unit: Operations – addition

**Today's Marks:** ____ /4

## Day Two Try these.

**1** At an ice-cream parlour, a group of Beaver Scouts bought **4** vanilla cones, **10** chocolate cones and **6** strawberry cones. How many cones did they buy altogether?

Answer: _____ Marks: __ /1

**2** Olivia's scooter has **3** wheels. How many **wheels** are there altogether on 8 identical scooters?

Answer: _____ Marks: __ /2

**3** Fill in the missing numbers in the magic square. The numbers in each row (across) and column (down) must add up to **17**.

| 3 |   | 12 |
|---|---|----|
|   | 3 |    |
|   |   | 0  |

Marks: __ /5

> **Keyword**
> A row is **horizontal**. Horizontal means going from side to side.
> A column is **vertical**. Vertical means going up and down.

## Puzzle Power ✏️

The code for this lock has 4 digits. Find the first two digits by adding 9 and 7. Find the last two digits by adding 13 and 18. What is the code?

Today's Marks: __ /8

## Day Three  Try these.

1. In the first half of a basketball game, the Wildcats scored **26** points. In the third quarter, they scored **13** points and in the last quarter, they scored **17** points. How many points did they have then?

Answer: _____   Marks: _____ /1

2. **Thirty-six** passengers were on a bus travelling from Kildare to Dublin. **Eight** more passengers got on at Newbridge. How many passengers were on the bus then?

Answer: _____   Marks: _____ /1

3. Using each of the digits 1, 2, 3, 4, 5, 6, 7, 8 only once, fill in

| Row 1 | | + | | + | | + | | = | |
|---|---|---|---|---|---|---|---|---|---|
| Row 2 | | + | | + | | + | | = | |

the table so that both rows add up to the same number.

Marks: _____ /2

## Puzzle power

You can play this game with up to four players. Each player needs a different coloured pencil.

1. Roll a pair of dice, add the two numbers and colour in a square with your total on the grid.

2. The next player takes their turn.

3. The first player to colour four touching squares is the winner.

| 8 | 2 | 7 | 11 | 3 | 9 | 6 |
|---|---|---|---|---|---|---|
| 4 | 10 | 5 | 12 | 9 | 2 | 11 |
| 7 | 3 | 8 | 10 | 5 | 8 | 4 |
| 9 | 11 | 4 | 2 | 6 | 12 | 9 |
| 6 | 10 | 7 | 5 | 3 | 8 | 9 |
| 10 | 7 | 2 | 11 | 6 | 3 | 12 |

Today's Marks: _____ /4

## Day Four  Try these.

**1** There are **52** white keys and **36** black keys on a piano. How many keys are there altogether?

Answer: _____  Marks: ____ /1

**2** Ciarán played two games of Subway Surfers. He scored **48** points in the first game and **27** points in the second game. How many points did he score in total?

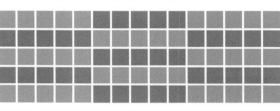

Answer: ____  Marks: ____ /1

**3** This diagram shows the tiles on a hallway floor. How many **(a)** blue and **(b)** red tiles are there? **(c)** How many tiles are there in total?

**Top Tip!**
Skip count in 5s.

Answers: (a) _____  (b) _____  (c) _____  Marks: ____ /3

## Super Sleuth investigates

Today's Marks: ____ /5

In rugby, you get 5 points for a try. You get 2 points if you kick the ball over the bar after a try. During a recent match, Connacht scored 3 tries. The captain kicked the ball over the bar twice, but he missed on his third attempt.

1. How many points did Connacht score with their 3 tries?

2. How many points did they score by kicking the ball over the bar?

**Team Talk**
Reader
Calculator
Checker
Reporter

Total Marks: ____ /21   Got this!  ◯  Getting there. ◯ ◯  Need help!  ◯

My favourite activity was _____

# 6 Revision 1

## Polar Opposites!

**Day One** Try these.

**1** Emperor penguins live in Antarctica, which is near the South Pole. They cannot fly, but they use their wings for diving. **Estimate** how many wings there are in this image.

**Answer:** **Marks:** /1

**2** A fisherman caught a number of shellfish near Antarctica in a week. **(a)** Put the number of shellfish caught in order from the **largest** number to the smallest number caught.

| 159 | 155 | 161 | 160 | 158 | 157 | 156 |
|---|---|---|---|---|---|---|
|  |  |  |  |  |  |  |

**(b)** What was the **3rd highest** number of shellfish caught?

**Answer: (b)** **Marks:** /2

**3** A group of scientists in Antarctica received three food parcels. One parcel weighed **eighty kg**, another weighed **one less** than eighty kg and the last one weighed **one more** than eighty kg. Write the weight of the lightest parcel in digits.

**Answer:** **Marks:** /1

**Strand:** Number **Strand Units:** Counting and Numeration; Comparing and Ordering; Place Value; Operations – addition **Today's Marks:** /4

## Day Two Try these.

**1** **40** Arctic explorers were on their way to the **North Pole**. If they broke up into groups of **ten**, how many groups were there?

Answer: _____ Marks: \_\_\_ /1

**2** The explorers saw seals, polar bears and walruses on a big iceberg. They counted **64** seals, **31** fewer polar bears than seals and **15** more walruses than polar bears. **(a)** How many polar bears and walruses were there altogether? **(b)** Was this less than or greater than the number of seals? Write your answer using < or >.

Answers: (a) _____ (b) _____ Marks: \_\_\_ /4

**3** Back at base camp, explorers Omar and Cathal played a game of chess. Omar made the 1st move, Cathal made the 2nd move and so on. Whose turn was it on the 7th move? Fill in the table to work out the answer.

| 1st move | Omar |
|----------|--------|
| 2nd move | Cathal |
|          |        |
|          |        |
|          |        |
|          |        |
|          |        |

Answer: _____ Marks: \_\_\_ /1

Today's Marks: \_\_\_ /6

## Day Three   Try these.

**1** Sally and Pete were on a flight to Lapland, which is in the Arctic Circle. They played cards to pass the time. If you add the numbers on their cards together, did Pete have more than or less than Sally? Write your answer using < or >.

| Sally's cards | | Pete's cards | |
|---|---|---|---|

Answer: _____   Marks: ___ /1

**2** Sally wanted to take lots of photographs of the animals in Lapland. She bought camera batteries in packs of **ten**. If she had **63** batteries, **(a)** how many full packs did she have? **(b)** How many batteries were left over?

**Top Tip!**

Draw a picture.

Answers: (a) ____  (b) ____  Marks: ____ /2

**3** At the Lapland Market, Pete saw lots of chocolate reindeer for sale. There were 10 − 9 in the **hundreds** place, 2 + 4 in the **tens** place and 3 + 5 in the **units** place. Write the number of **hundreds** on the top shelf, **tens** on the middle shelf and **units** on the bottom shelf.

Answer: _____   Marks: ____ /3

**4** The Lapland Market also had lots of warm jackets for sale. There were **7 tens** and **14 units** for sale. How many groups of ten were there?

Answer: _____   Marks: ____ /1

Today's Marks: ____ /7

## Day Four Try these.

**1** During a sleigh ride, there were **5** children in a red sleigh, **10** in a green sleigh and **5** in a black sleigh. How many children were in sleighs altogether?

**Top Tip!**
Remember doubles when adding. Which numbers add up to 10?

Answer: | Marks: | /1

**2** Georgina collected pine cones in Lapland. She collected **26** the first day and **10** more the following day. How many pine cones did she collect in total?

Answer: | Marks: | /2

**3** At the Ice-cream Igloo, **twenty-four** strawberry milkshakes, **forty-three** chocolate milkshakes and **twenty-six** vanilla milkshakes were sold. How many milkshakes were sold altogether?

Answer: | Marks: | /3

Today's Marks: | /6

## Super Sleuth investigates

A group of explorers at the North Pole ate 5 packs of beans and 6 packs of spaghetti hoops.

4 tins per pack    3 tins per pack

1. How many tins of beans did they eat?

2. How many tins of spaghetti hoops did they eat?

### Team Talk

Reader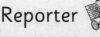
Calculator
Checker
Reporter

Total Marks: | /23

31

# 7 Strategy: Act it Out

**Day One** Try these.

Today, we will use lollipop sticks to help us break down each number story.

The act-it-out strategy helps you to break down a number story by using concrete materials. This might involve using blocks, unifix cubes, counters, lollipop sticks, playing cards or money to act out the story, making it easier for you to understand. This strategy can be fun if you like to be active while you work!

**1** Jane has **12** puppies. She wants to place an equal number of puppies in each basket. How many should she place in each basket? Draw your answer.

Marks: /1

**2** Bruce bought **5** *Batman* comics. With each comic, there were **3** superhero stickers to collect. How many stickers did he have?

Answer:      Marks: /1

**3** Dean has **10** computer games. Hazel has **double** that amount and Dawn has **10 more** than Hazel. If you were to share the games evenly, how many would they each get?

Answer:      Marks: /2

**4** Look at the image. The artist got the sum wrong! Can you move just one matchstick to correct the sum?

Answer:      Marks: /1

Today's Marks:    /5

**Day Two** Try these.

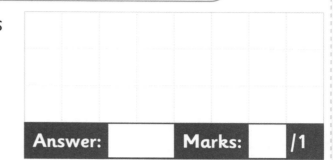

Today, we will use blocks and playing cards to help us break down number stories.

**1** Magda built a tower with **4** rows of blocks. She used **3** blocks in each row. How many blocks did she use altogether?

Answer:     Marks:    /1

**2** If **3** blocks are used to make 2 steps, how many blocks are used to make 3 steps?

Answer:     Marks:    /1

**3** Look at the playing cards below. You will see 2 different ways to arrange a king, a queen and a Jack. In the table, write the 4 other ways that these cards can be arranged.

king    queen    Jack

king    Jack    queen

| 1. | king | queen | Jack |
|----|------|-------|------|
| 2. | king | Jack | queen |
| 3. | | | |
| 4. | | | |
| 5. | | | |
| 6. | | | |

**Top Tip!**
Act it out with real playing cards.

Marks:    /4

**4** Stephen and Alice have **9** playing cards each. They have made up a game. Every time Stephen loses **1** card, Alice loses **3**. When Alice has lost all of her cards, how many will Stephen have left?

**Top Tip!**
Act it out with real playing cards.

Answer:     Marks:    /1

**Day Three** Try these.

Today, we will use counters and money to help us break down number stories.

① Ahmed has a **red** T-shirt, a **blue** T-shirt, a pair of yellow shorts and a pair of **green** shorts. In the table, write the 4 different outfits that he could make with these items of clothing. Use counters to help you.

| | T-shirt | Shorts |
|---|---|---|
| **1.** | | |
| **2.** | | |
| **3.** | | |
| **4.** | | |

Marks: ☐ /4

② Sabrina has **4** hair bobbins: **1 pink**, **1 blue**, **1 purple** and **1** yellow. She always wears two bobbins in her hair and they are always two different colours. In pairs, discuss how many different combinations of colours she could wear in her hair.

Marks: ☐ /6

③ Owen wants to buy a bar costing **25c**. In the table, can you write 4 different ways that he could pay for the bar using the coins shown? You can use the same coin more than once in your answers. Use money to help you.

| 1. | 20c + |
|---|---|
| 2. | |
| 3. | |
| 4. | |

Marks: ☐ /4

Today's Marks: ☐ /14

## Day Four  Try these.

Today, we will act it out to help us break down each number story.

C LUE s

**1** How many $\frac{1}{4}$ litre bottles can you fill from 1 litre of water? Act it out.

Answer: ___ Marks: ___ /1

**2** Jenna is sitting in front of Bill. Bill is sitting beside Adam. Adam is sitting behind Fionn. Who is sitting beside Jenna? Act it out in groups of 4.

Answer: ___ Marks: ___ /1

**3** Chris works in the library and there are four piles of books that he needs to put back on the shelves.

- 4 of the books are nature books.
- There are twice as many history books as nature books.
- There are twice as many fiction books as history books.
- There are 5 more science books than fiction books.

How many **(a)** history, **(b)** fiction and **(c)** science books are there?

Answers: (a) ___ (b) ___ (c) ___ Marks: ___ /3

## Super Sleuth challenge

Today's Marks: ___ /5

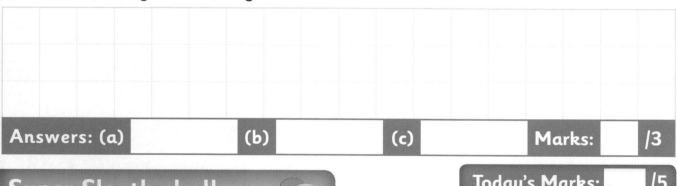

In PE, 30 children were playing the game 'Human Knot'. They were playing in groups of either 10 or 5. How many different groups might there have been? Draw the groups.

Total Marks: ___ /31   Got this! 👍 ⬤   Getting there. ✍ ⬤   Need help! 👎 ⬤

I helped my friend by ___

35

# 8  Subtraction

**We are learning to:** Make number sentences for number stories involving subtraction within 99. ☐ Solve two-step word puzzles involving addition and subtraction. ☐

**Day One** Look at the example below.

Taylor bought a packet of 25 stamps. She used 10 stamps to post cards to her cousins. How many stamps does she have left?

**CLUES**

**C**ircle the numbers and keywords:
25 stamps, used 10, how many does she have left?

**L**ink with operation needed (+ or −): Subtract (−).

**U**se a strategy: Draw a bar model.

**E**stimate and calculate:

25 stamps

| 1 | 2 | 3 | 4 | 5 | 6 | 7 | 8 | 9 | 10 | 11 | 12 | 13 | 14 | 15 | 16 | 17 | 18 | 19 | 20 | 21 | 22 | 23 | 24 | 25 |

Used 10

**Answer:**
15

**S**ummarise how you got your answer:
I drew a bar and split it into 25 parts. I crossed out 10 stamps and saw that there were 15 left.

Try these.

**CLUES**

1. There were **27** slices of bread in a packet. Ann Marie used **14** slices to make toast. How many slices were left?

Answer:

Marks: /1

2. There were **36** chicken nuggets in the freezer. Grandad cooked **6** for Leah and **6** for Ben. How many were left in the freezer?

Answer:

Marks: /2

3. **48** children were at a birthday party. **15** children went home early. How many children stayed?

Answer:

Marks: /1

**Strand:** Number **Strand Unit:** Operations – subtraction

**Today's Marks:** /4

**Day Two** Try these.

**1** There were 56 basketballs on sale at the National Basketball Arena. 14 basketballs were sold on Saturday. By how much is **14** less than **56**?

Answer: _____ Marks: _____ /1

**2** Thirty-six children took part in a race. Twelve of them were boys. By how much is **thirty-six** greater than **twelve**?

Answer: _____ Marks: _____ /1

**3** Kristina made **36** chocolate rice crispie buns. She decorated **14** with jellies, **11** with cherries and left the rest plain. How many were plain?

Answer: _____ Marks: _____ /2

**4** At the Knights' Academy, there are two classes, with **25** students in one and **28** in the other. At the School of Dragon Taming, there are only **26** students. **(a)** How many students are there at the Knights' Academy altogether? **(b)** How many more students are there at the Knights' Academy than at the School of Dragon Taming?

Answers: (a) _____ (b) _____ Marks: _____ /2

**Team Talk**

Reader
Calculator
Checker
Reporter

Today's Marks: _____ /6

37

**Day Three** Try these.

1. Tanya saved up **€48**. She spent **€6** on a Disney colouring book, **€5** on markers and **€4** on glitter glue. How much money did she have left?

Answer: € _____ Marks: ___ /2

2. Laois scored **24** points in a hurling match. Dublin scored **5** points less than Laois. How many points did the two teams score in total?

Answer: _____ Marks: ___ /2

3. Ciarán had **26** songs on his iPod. He **deleted** 3 songs on Monday, **4** on Tuesday, **5** on Wednesday and **3** on Thursday. How many songs were left on his iPod? Use the table to help you.

| Monday | 26 – 3 = |
|---|---|
| | |
| | |
| | |

Answer: _____ Marks: ___ /3

**Puzzle power**

Run for your life! You must climb the pyramid to escape the mummy. Place the numbers 1 to 6 in the blocks so that the difference between two numbers next to each other is equal to the number above them.

Today's Marks: _____ /7

## Day Four  Try these.

**1** Seán baked a number of gingerbread men. He sold **25** at a cake sale and gave **3** to his principal. The last **2** gingerbread men ran off before anyone could eat them! How many gingerbread men did Seán bake?

Answer: _____  Marks: _____ /1

**2** Callum tidied up his tablet. He deleted **5** old games and downloaded **7** new games. If he now has **17** games, how many did he start with?

Answer: _____  Marks: _____ /2

**3** **28** passengers got off a bus when it reached the shopping centre. Before the shopping centre, the bus had stopped at a hospital, where **8** passengers got off and **4** got on. How many passengers were on the bus just before it stopped at the hospital?

Answer: _____  Marks: _____ /2

Today's Marks: _____ /5

## Super Sleuth investigates

Dean works in a biscuit factory. He has to make sure that there are **22** chocolate finger biscuits in each box. One day, he finds two boxes with the wrong amount. The first box contains **29** biscuits and the second contains **33**.

1. How many biscuits should he remove from the first box?

2. How many biscuits should he remove from the second box?

3. How many biscuits will he remove altogether?

**Team Talk**

Reader

Calculator

Checker

Reporter

Total Marks: _____ /22    Got this!  ⚪    Getting there.  ⚪    Need help!  ⚪

I loved doing _____

 **9** Spatial Awareness

We are learning to: Explore and use the language of spatial relations. ☐
Give and follow simple directions. ☐

**Day One** Look at the example below.

Adam and Cian share a bunk bed. If Adam has to climb up the ladder to go to bed, which bunk does each boy sleep on?

**C**ircle the numbers and keywords:
Adam and Cian, bunk bed, up the ladder

**L**ink with operation needed (+ or –): None

**U**se a strategy: Draw a picture.

**E**stimate and calculate:

**Answer:**
Adam sleeps on the top bunk and Cian sleeps on the bottom bunk.

**S**ummarise how you got your answer:
Adam has to climb up the ladder, so he sleeps on the top bunk and Cian sleeps on the bottom bunk.

**Try these.**

1. Draw a rug underneath the couch. Draw a cat sitting on the right-hand cushion of the couch. Draw a book on the left-hand cushion.

   Marks: ☐ /3

2. Tick the correct sentence.

   ■ The microwave is between the toaster and the kettle. ☐

   ■ The toaster is between the kettle and the microwave. ☐

   ■ The kettle is between the microwave and the toaster. ☐

Marks: ☐ /1

Today's Marks: ☐ /4

**Day Two** Try these.

**1** (a) Tick the correct sentence.

- The basketball is on the table.

- The basketball is underneath the table.

- The basketball is to the right of the table.

(b) Draw a vase of flowers on top of the table.

**Marks:** [  ] /2

**2** The first clock shows 12 o'clock.

(a) If the big hand goes to 6, does it make a **quarter** turn or a **half** turn? (b) What number would the big hand have gone to, if it had made the other turn?

**Answers:** (a) [                    ] (b) [                    ] **Marks:** [  ] /2

**3** Using **only** the directions 'Turn right' or 'Turn left', help the wizard to get to the red door at the top of the maze. The first 3 are written for you. Turn the page around to help you with the directions.

| 1. Turn right. | 2. Turn right. |
|---|---|
| 3. Turn left. | 4. |
| 5. | 6. |
| 7. | 8. |
| 9. | 10. |
| 11. | 12. |
| 13. | 14. |

**Marks:** [  ] /11

**Today's Marks:** [  ] /15   41

**Day Three** Try these.

 **1** The teacher is at the front of the school and the door is locked.
**(a)** Tick the sentence that explains how he can get to the car park behind the school.

- He can go through the school.

- He can go over the school.

- He can go around the school.

- He can go under the school.

**(b)** The teacher walks past the wall with 2 windows. Should he turn left or right to get to the car park?

| Answer: (b) | Marks: | /2 |
|---|---|---|

 **2** **(a)** Tick the correct sentence.

- The red car is to the right of the blue car.

- The red car is between the blue car and the green car.

- The green car is to the right of the blue car.

**(b)** If the blue car went in front of the red car, would the first, the second or the third sentence above be true?

| Answer: (b) | Marks: | /2 |
|---|---|---|

 **3** Write four directions to help Carla reach the sandpit.

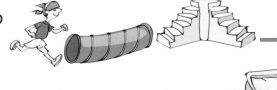

**Answers:**

1.

2.

3.

4.

Marks: /4

Today's Marks: /8

**Day Four** Try these.

**Top Tip!**

The hands on a clock turn in this direction.

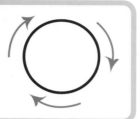

① Look at the image above. Damian is facing the cat. If he makes a **quarter** turn in the direction that the hands on a clock turn, what will he end up facing?

Answer: _____  Marks: ___ /1

② Look at the image above again. This time, if Damian makes a **half** turn, followed by a **quarter** turn, followed by another **half** turn (in the direction that the hands on a clock turn), what will he end up facing?

**Top Tip!**

Act it out.

Answer: _____  Marks: ___ /2

③ Which **two** matchsticks could you move to make three squares in this matchstick puzzle? Draw a diagram showing how the puzzle would look after moving the two matchsticks.

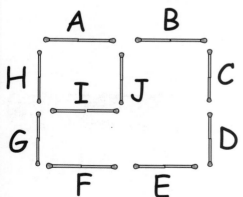

Answer: _____  Marks: ___ /3

Today's Marks: ___ /6

Total Marks: ___ /33

Got this!  ○  Getting there.  ○  Need help!  ○

I would like to get better at _____

Week 9 | Spatial Awareness

43

# 10  Fractions

**We are learning to:**

Identify halves and quarters. ☐ Calculate half or a quarter of a set up to 20. ☐

## Day One — Look at the example below.

Rita had 4 hairbands. She gave $\frac{1}{4}$ of them to Sophia. How many hairbands did she give to Sophia?

**CLUES**

**C**ircle the numbers and keywords: 4 hairbands, gave $\frac{1}{4}$ to Sophia

**L**ink with operation needed (+ or −): None

**U**se a strategy: Draw a picture.

**E**stimate and calculate:
$\frac{1}{4}$ means 1 out of 4.

**Answer:**
1

**S**ummarise how you got your answer:
I know that $\frac{1}{4}$ is 1 out of 4, so I knew that Rita gave 1 of the 4 hairbands to Sophia.

## Try these.

**CLUES**

1. Mars has **two** moons named Phobos and Deimos. Earth has **half** that amount. How many moons do they have altogether?

   **Answer:** ___ **Marks:** ___ /1

2. Conor had **4** oranges. He cut all of them in half. How many halves did he have?

   **Answer:** ___ **Marks:** ___ /1

3. Noel's granny gave him €12 and told him to give **half** to his sister. Noel then spent **half** of his share on a slushie. How much money did he have left?

   **Answer: €** ___ **Marks:** ___ /3

**Today's Marks:** ___ /5

## Day Two Try these.

**1** David went bowling. On his first go, he knocked down $\frac{1}{2}$ of the bowling pins. How many bowling pins was that?

Answer: _____ Marks: _____ /1

**2** Kate made a cheesecake. She gave $\frac{1}{4}$ to her granny, $\frac{1}{4}$ to her aunt and $\frac{1}{4}$ to her cousin. What fraction of the cheesecake did she have left?

Answer: _____ Marks: _____ /1

**3** (a) Josh wants to cut the Swiss roll into **4** equal slices. Draw 3 lines to show where he should cut it. (b) If he cut 2 Swiss rolls like this, how many slices would he have?

Answer: (b) _____ Marks: _____ /2

**4** On Saturday, Donal's dad brought home 12 doughnuts. Using the information below, write how many doughnuts were eaten each day in the table.

- On Saturday, $\frac{1}{2}$ of the doughnuts were eaten.
- On Sunday, 2 doughnuts were eaten.
- On Monday, $\frac{1}{2}$ of the remaining doughnuts were eaten.
- On Tuesday, the last of the doughnuts were eaten.

Marks: _____ /4

| Day | Doughnuts eaten |
|---|---|
| Saturday | |
| Sunday | |
| Monday | |
| Tuesday | |

Today's Marks: _____ /8

**Day Three** Try these.

C**LUE**'s

**1** Andrea and Jake are each painting part of their garden fence.
**(a)** What fraction of Andrea's part is painted? **(b)** What fraction of Jake's part does he still have left to paint?

Answers: (a) ___ (b) ___ Marks: ___ /2

**2** There were **12** children at a birthday party. $\frac{1}{4}$ of them did not eat any cake. **(a)** How many children did not eat cake? **(b)** How many children did eat cake?

**Top Tip!**
Act it out with counters.

Answers: (a) _____ (b) _____ Marks: ___ /2

**3** Donna got a box of chocolates for her birthday. After she had shared out the chocolates, there were 5 left. This was $\frac{1}{4}$ of the box. How many chocolates were in the box at the start?

Answer: ___ Marks: ___ /1

**Puzzle Power** ✏

Help the bear to find a path through the fraction maze to the honey!

| $\frac{1}{2}$ of 6 | 3 | $\frac{1}{2}$ of 10 | 6 | $\frac{1}{2}$ of 16 |
| 5 | | 5 | | 3 |
| $\frac{1}{2}$ of 20 | 5 | $\frac{1}{2}$ of 2 | 1 | $\frac{1}{2}$ of 12 |
| 3 | | 3 | | 6 |
| $\frac{1}{2}$ of 4 | 2 | $\frac{1}{2}$ of 8 | 7 | $\frac{1}{2}$ of 14 |
| 1 | | 4 | | 3 |
| $\frac{1}{2}$ of 10 | 7 | $\frac{1}{2}$ of 18 | 9 | $\frac{1}{2}$ of 4 | 2 → |

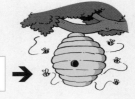

Today's Marks: ___ /5

## Day Four  Try these.

CLUEs

**1** **8** sausages were shared equally between **4** children. What fraction of the sausages did each child get?

**Top Tip!**
Draw a picture.

Answer: _____ Marks: ___ /1

**2** Tracy's mum cut 1 full wrap in half to make 2 half wraps. How many full wraps did she cut to make **6 half wraps** for lunch?

Answer: _____ Marks: ___ /2

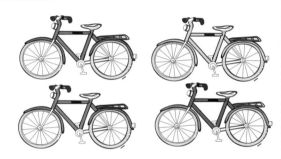

**3** In a class of **16** pupils, **8** pupils own a bicycle. 2 girls own a red bicycle, 2 girls own a yellow bicycle, 2 boys own a green bicycle and 2 boys own a blue bicycle.

**(a)** What fraction of the class own a bicycle?

**(b)** What fraction of the pupils who own a bicycle are girls?

**(c)** What fraction of all of the bicycles are **green**?

**Team Talk**

Reader

Calculator

Checker

Reporter

Answers: (a) ___ (b) ___ (c) ___ Marks: ___ /3

Today's Marks: ___ /6

Total Marks: ___ /24   Got this!  ● Getting there.  ● Need help!  ●

I enjoyed _____

# 11  2-D Shapes

**We are learning to:** Name and describe 2-D shapes. ☐
Combine and separate 2-D shapes. ☐ Identify halves of 2-D Shapes. ☐

## Day One Look at the example below.

Abram is painting 3 rectangular sheets of paper red to make a birthday banner for his sister. How many corners will he paint?

 **CLUES**

**C**ircle the numbers and keywords:
  3 sheets of A4 paper, how many corners?

**L**ink with operation needed (+ or −): Add (+).

**U**se a strategy: Draw a picture. ☐ ☐ ☐

**E**stimate and calculate:
  There are 4 corners on a rectangle.

  3 sheets of paper:
  4 + 4 + 4 = 12

  **Answer:**
  12 corners

**S**ummarise how you got your answer:
  I counted 4 corners on a rectangular sheet of paper. Abram has 3 sheets, so I added the corners using repeated addition.

## Try these.

 **CLUES**

1) Toby spreads Nutella on his cream crackers, touching all of the sides. If he makes **2** Nutella crackers, how many sides does he touch?

Answer: ☐ Marks: ☐ /1

2) Kelly's class are making clock faces with two different colours for times past and times to the hour. **(a)** What type of shape must they colour? **(b)** If they make **10** clock faces, how many of this shape are there?

Answers (a): ☐
(b) ☐ Marks: ☐ /2

3) Granny likes cutting sandwiches into shapes. If she makes 4 triangles, 2 squares and 3 rectangles, how many corners are there in total?

Answer: ☐ Marks: ☐ /3

**Today's Marks:** ☐ /6

# Day Two Try these.

**1** (a) How many rectangles can you see in the soccer pitch?
(b) How many curved shapes can you see?

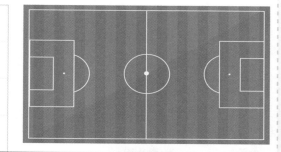

**Answers: (a)** _____ **(b)** _____ **Marks:** ____ **/2**

**2** Debbie's teacher asked her to draw a wallpaper design by joining two 2-D shapes. Look at her design below. How many corners can you see altogether in (a) the blue shapes and (b) the green shapes? (c) Draw your own wallpaper design using these two shapes.

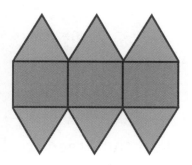

**Answers: (a)** ____ **(b)** ____ **Marks:** ____ **/3**

**3** 5 square napkins have each been placed on a round plate on a restaurant table. How many sides do the napkins and the plates have in total?

**Answer:** _____ **Marks:** ____ **/1**

## Super Sleuth challenge

Pick a flag and name the shapes in it. Count the corners, sides and how many 4-sided shapes and triangles there are.

**Today's Marks:** ____ **/6**

49

## Day Three  Try these.

**1** **(a)** If a racing car drives all the way around the edge of a roundabout once, what shape does it make?
**(b)** If two racing cars drive all the way around the edge of a roundabout **twice each**, how many of this shape do they make?

**Top Tip!**
Draw a picture.

Answers: (a) _____ (b) _____  Marks: ___ /2

**2** Hannah's mum made a big pancake that she wanted to share equally between 4 children.

**(a)** Draw 2 lines to show how you would cut the pancake into 4 equal parts.

**(b)** Did you cut the pancake into halves or quarters?

Answer: (b) _____  Marks: ___ /2

**3** Miss Casey brought her class of 20 pupils out to the green for PE and asked them what sport they wanted to play.

- $\frac{1}{4}$ of the class wanted to play soccer.
- $\frac{1}{4}$ of the class wanted to play rounders.
- $\frac{1}{2}$ of the class wanted to play hurling.

Miss Casey used cones to create an area on the green for each group. Draw two lines to show where the areas were split up, making sure that there is enough space based on the size of each group. Write the name of each sport in the correct area.

Marks: ___ /3

Today's Marks: ___ /7

**Day Four** Try these.

1 **(a)** Name 4 different 2-D shapes that you can see in the painting. **(b)** How many corners are there altogether on the blue building with 5 windows and a purple door?

Answer: (a)

(b)　　　　Marks:　/5

2 How many triangles can you see? (Be careful! There are more than meets the eye at first!)

Answer:　　　Marks:　/1

3 Design a city scene using 2-D shapes. You can use as many shapes as you like, but you must include:

| oval | rectangle | triangle | circle | square | semi-circle |
|---|---|---|---|---|---|

Marks:　/6

**Super Sleuth challenge**

Today's Marks:　/12

Using four colours, explore different ways of colouring in these triangles.

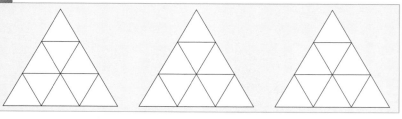

# 12 Revision 2

## Perfect Pastimes

### Day One Try these.

1. There were **25** children in a Beaver Scouts group. If **11** of them were boys, how many girls were in the group?

Answer: ☐ Marks: ☐ /1

2. Fastnet basketball team scored **45** points. Rangers basketball team scored **12** points **less** than Fastnet. How many points did Rangers score?

Answer: ☐ Marks: ☐ /1

3. On Monday morning, there were **30** families staying at a campsite.

- On Monday afternoon, 5 families left and 2 families arrived.
- On Tuesday, 7 families left and 3 families arrived.
- On Wednesday, 8 families left and 6 families arrived.

**Team Talk**

Reader
Calculator
Checker
Reporter

How many families were staying at the campsite by the end of the day on Wednesday? Use the table to help you.

| | Starting Number | Out | In | | End of Day |
|---|---|---|---|---|---|
| **Monday** | 30 | − 5 | + 2 | = | |
| **Tuesday** | | | | = | |
| **Wednesday** | | | | = | |

Answer: ☐ Marks: ☐ /3

Strand: **Number** Strand Units: Operations − subtraction; Fractions
Strand: Shape and Space Strand Units: Spatial Awareness; 2-D Shapes

**Today's Marks:** ☐ /5

**Day Two** Try these.

**1** **(a)** Look at the image and tick the correct sentence.

- The scuba diver is below the boat.
- The scuba diver is above the boat.
- The scuba diver is in the boat.

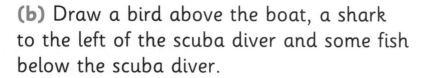

**(b)** Draw a bird above the boat, a shark to the left of the scuba diver and some fish below the scuba diver.

**Marks:** ☐ /2

**2** A tour bus is on its way to Tayto Park. **(a)** In which direction should the driver turn when she reaches sign **A**? **(b)** In which direction should she **not** turn when she reaches sign **B**?

**Answers: (a)** ☐ **(b)** ☐ **Marks:** ☐ /2

**3** Tom's favourite pastime is reading. He has started at a new school and needs help finding the library. He can't go down certain corridors. Can you give him directions? The first two directions have been written for you.

**Team Talk**

Reader
Calculator
Checker
Reporter

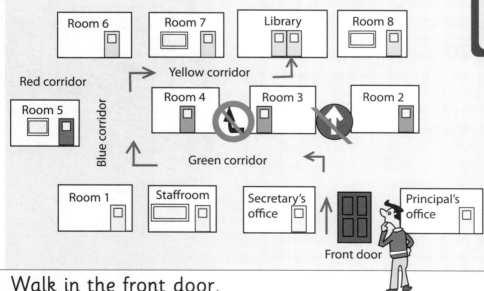

| 1. | Walk in the front door. |
| 2. | Turn left onto the green corridor. |
| 3. | |
| 4. | |
| 5. | |

**Marks:** ☐ /3

## Day Three  Try these.

**1** Seán was learning how to bake. He bought a carton of **12** eggs and used one-quarter of them to bake a sponge cake. How many eggs did he use?

**Top Tip!**
Draw a picture.

Answer: _____ Marks: ___ /1

**2** Selina had **€20** and decided to knit a scarf for her grandad. She spent **half** of her money on wool and **half** of what was left on new knitting needles. **(a)** How much did she spend on the knitting needles? **(b)** How much money did she have left after buying the wool and the knitting needles?

Answers: (a) € _____ (b) € _____ Marks: ___ /2

**3** Yusuf was having a sleepover and decided to make a fruit salad for his friends. In his fridge, there were **12** strawberries, **20** blueberries, **16** grapes and **18** raspberries. Fill in the table to work out how many pieces of fruit he used in total.

**He used …**

| | | |
|---|---|---|
| $\frac{1}{2}$ of the strawberries | = | |
| $\frac{1}{4}$ of the blueberries | = | |
| $\frac{1}{4}$ of the grapes | = | |
| $\frac{1}{2}$ of the raspberries | = | |
| **Total pieces of fruit** | | |

Answer: _____ Marks: ___ /5

Today's Marks: ___ /8

## Day Four Try these.

**1** At a Beaver Scouts Den, **5** children were competing to see who could hula-hoop the longest. Each child had **2** hula-hoops around their waist. **(a)** How many hula-hoops were there in total? **(b)** What kind of 2-D shape is a hula-hoop?

Answers: (a) ☐ (b) ☐ Marks: ☐ /2

**2** At the Beaver Scouts Den, **7** rectangles were drawn on the ground for a hopscotch game. How many sides and corners were there in total?

Answer: ☐ Marks: ☐ /2

**3** The Beaver Scout Leaders hung bunting around the games room for Sunday Funday. The flags on the bunting were 2-D shapes and there were 30 sides in total. What shape do you think was used to make the flags?

Answer: ☐

Marks: ☐ /1

Today's Marks: ☐ /5

## Puzzle power

Super Sleuth loves doing tangram puzzles in his spare time. A tangram is made up of a square cut into seven 2-D shapes as shown.

One of the images below is **not** made up of all of the tangram shapes shown above. Help Super Sleuth to detect which one is the fake. You might find it helpful to number the shapes to match the numbers above.

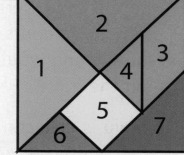

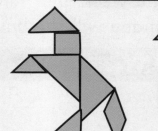

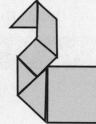

# 13  Strategy: Identifying Patterns

**Day One** Look at the example below.

The strategy of identifying patterns helps you to see how shapes, pictures or numbers are repeated in a number story. Look at the pattern below and say the shapes out loud. What comes next?

Read the number pattern below out loud. What comes next?

0,   2,   4,   6,   8,   ☐ ,   ☐ ,   ☐
(+2) (+2) (+2) (+2) (+2)   (+2)   (+2)

**Try these.**                                                      **CLUES**

1) Mike is making a tile pattern above his bathroom sink. Can you finish the pattern for him?

**Marks:** ☐ /1

2) A group of acrobats have made a human pyramid. There are 3 acrobats at the bottom, standing on a mat. There are 2 more standing on their shoulders and there is 1 more standing on *their* shoulders at the very top. If they were to add another row of acrobats at the bottom, how many would be standing on the mat?

**Answer:** ☐   **Marks:** ☐ /2

3) Sally is collecting Shopkin toys. She buys 5 in the 1st week, 7 in the 2nd week and 9 in the 3rd week. If she continues this pattern, how many will she buy in the 7th week? Use the table to help you.

| Week 1 | Week 2 | Week 3 | Week 4 | Week 5 | Week 6 | Week 7 |
|--------|--------|--------|--------|--------|--------|--------|
| 5 | 7 | 9 | | | | |

**Answer:** ☐   **Marks:** ☐ /4

**Today's Marks:** ☐ /7

**Day Two** Try these.

Use the strategy of identifying patterns to solve each number story below.

① Starting on Monday, Shane went to his granny's house every second day after school. On which other two school days did he go to her house?

Answer: _____ Marks: [ ] /1

② **(a)** Michaela was painting her nails with a pattern of **purple**, yellow, **purple**, yellow. If she continued this pattern, what colour did she use for the little finger on her right hand? **(b)** If Michaela also painted her sister's nails with the same pattern, how many nails were painted yellow in total?

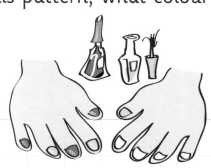

Answers: (a) _____ (b) _____ Marks: [ ] /2

③ A teacher brought **12** girls and **8** boys to a puppet theatre. There were 20 seats in a row. The teacher asked the children to start off sitting in the following pattern: **boy**, **girl**, **boy**, **girl**, and so on. Will there be a boy or a girl sitting in **(a)** the 6th seat and **(b)** the 19th seat? (Hint: How might you use numbers and colours in the diagram below to help you?)

**Team Talk**

Reader
Calculator
Checker
Reporter

| A row of 20 seats |
|---|

| | | | | | | | | | | | | | | | | | | | |
|---|---|---|---|---|---|---|---|---|---|---|---|---|---|---|---|---|---|---|---|

Answers: (a) _____ (b) _____ Marks: [ ] /2

Today's Marks: [ ] /5

**Day Three** Try these.

Use the strategy of identifying patterns to solve each number story below.

**1** Sarah was planting a row of tulips with the following pattern: **pink**, yellow, orange, **pink**, yellow, orange. If she continued this pattern, what colour was the **10th** tulip?

**Top Tip!**
Draw a picture.

**Answer:** ☐ **Marks:** ☐ /1

**2** A waiter is laying a table for a wedding. He has to lay out five place settings like the **first one** shown below, but he has made **3** mistakes. Find the mistakes and mark them with an 'X'.

**Marks:** ☐ /3

**3** The school nurse came to check the eyesight of all of the students in Joe's class. She checked **4** students every hour and it took her **6** hours altogether. How many students had the nurse checked after **(a)** 4 hours and **(b)** 5 hours? **(c)** How many students were there in Joe's class altogether? (Hint: Complete the table and look for the pattern.)

| 1 hour | 4 students |
|---|---|
| 2 hours | 8 students |
| 3 hours | students |
| 4 hours | students |
| 5 hours | students |
| 6 hours | students |

**Answers: (a)** ☐ **(b)** ☐ **(c)** ☐ **Marks:** ☐ /3

**Today's Marks:** ☐ /7

**Day Four** Try these.

Use the strategy of identifying patterns to solve each number story below.

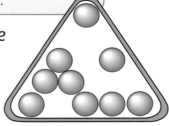

**1** In this snooker triangle, some of the red balls are missing. Draw the missing balls and then finish writing the number pattern. (Hint: The pattern begins with the first row at the top.)

Number pattern: 1, ___ , ___ , ___ , ___    Marks: ___ /1

**2** Keeley and her friend Jack are playing a game and Keeley really wants to be on. She says the rhyme, "Eeny, meeny, miney, moe, catch a tiger by its toe. If he screeches let him go. Eeny, meeny, miney moe." Who does Keeley need to start with in order for her to be on?

Answer: ___    Marks: ___ /1

**3** The ski lift can only carry the number of skiers shown in the image. How many ski lifts are needed to carry **15** skiers up the mountain?

**Top Tip!**
Skip count backwards.

Answer: ___    Marks: ___ /2

Today's Marks: ___ /4

## Super Sleuth investigates

Look at the image. This is a platform made of blocks on which 3 children can stand to receive medals.

1. How many blocks would you use to build a similar platform for 5 children?

2. How many blocks would you use to build a similar platform for 7 children?

**Team Talk**

Reader
Calculator
Checker
Reporter

Total Marks: ___ /23    Got this!  ◯ Getting there.  ◯ Need help!  ◯

I helped my friend by ___

59

# 14 Money

**We are learning to:** Recognise, exchange and use coins up to the value of €2. ☐

**Day One** Look at the example below.

Claire went to the school shop and bought a copy costing 50c and a pencil costing 20c. How much money did she spend in total?

**CLUES**

**C**ircle the numbers and keywords: 50c, 20c, in total

**L**ink with operation needed (+ or −): Add (+).

**U**se a strategy: Act it out.

**E**stimate and calculate:

My estimate:
less than €1

| T | U |
|---|---|
| 5 | 0 |
| +2 | 0 |
| 7 | 0 |

**Answer:**
70c

**S**ummarise how you got your answer:
I added the two amounts.

Try these.

**CLUES**

**1** Jane has **six** 10c coins. How much money does she have?

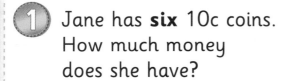

Answer: ___ Marks: ___ /1

**2** Ian bought a pack of 2 toothbrushes for **€1**. How much did each toothbrush cost?

Answer: ___ Marks: ___ /1

**3** A plain ice-cream cone costs **80c**. A large ice-cream cone with a Flake costs **€1.10**. How much **extra** does the large ice-cream cone cost?

Answer: ___ Marks: ___ /1

Strand: Measures Strand Unit: Money

Today's Marks: ___ /3

**Day Two** Try these.

**1** Nigel bought a packet of balloons costing **€1.50**. How much change did he get from **€2**? Draw the coins that he could have got as change. Use more than one.

Answer: ☐ Marks: ☐ /2

**2** McWimpy sells a hamburger for **€1.55**. Burger Hut sells a hamburger for **€0.95**. How much money would you **save** by buying the Burger Hut hamburger?

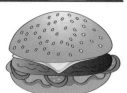

Answer: ☐ Marks: ☐ /1

**3** Emma's school was collecting money for charity. Emma brought in **20c** every week for **8** weeks. How much money did Emma give to the charity?

**Top Tip!**
Identify a pattern.

Answer: € ☐ Marks: ☐ /2

**4** Colm, Ciara and Trevor each decided to get their name printed on the back of their county jersey. They were charged **25c** for each letter in their names. How much did **(a)** Colm, **(b)** Ciara and **(c)** Trevor pay? Write your answers in euro and cent where possible.

**Team Talk**

Reader
Calculator
Checker
Reporter

Answers: (a) € ☐  (b) € ☐  (c) € ☐  Marks: ☐ /3

Today's Marks: ☐ /8

61

**Day Three** Try these.

**1** Molly's dad parked his car in a car park for **2** hours. The car park cost **55c** per hour. How much did he have to pay?

**Top Tip!**
Identify a pattern.

Answer: €          Marks:     /1

**2** Georgia downloaded a Star Wars game and a Minecraft game. How much did she pay for the two games altogether?

| Star Wars game | Minecraft game |
|---|---|

Answer: €          Marks:     /3

**3** Cian bought a bottle of water for **52c** and a sherbet dip for **39c**. **(a)** How much he spend? **(b)** How much change did he get from **€2**?

Answers: (a)               (b) €               Marks:     /2

**Puzzle power** ✏️

Snatch the loot from Captain Bluebeard! Make amounts totalling 50c by shading **down** or **across** the grid. How much loot will you manage to snatch altogether?

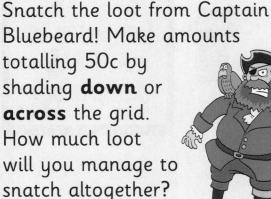

Today's Marks:          /6

## Day Four Try these.

**1** Olivia wants to buy a pair of sunglasses costing **150c**. She has **86c**. How much more money does she need?

Answer: | Marks: | /1

**2** Jamie bought **10** glow sticks for **100c**. **(a)** How much did he pay for each glow stick? **(b)** Jamie's friend Chris bought 3 glow sticks from Jamie. How much money did Chris pay Jamie?

Answers (a):

(b) | Marks: | /2

**3** Zoe wants to play an Angry Birds video game at the shopping centre. It costs **40c** for **3** games. How many games can she play for **120c**?

**Top Tip!**
Identify a pattern.

Answer: | Marks: | /2

Today's Marks: | /5

## Super Sleuth investigates

**Team Talk**

Reader
Calculator
Checker
Reporter

Ellie and Harry are at a funfair. Ellie has €1.55 and Harry has €2. Both children want to spend all of their money.

1. Which 3 amusements could Ellie choose?

2. Which 3 amusements could Harry choose?

| Funfair Price List | |
|---|---|
| Ferris wheel | 50c |
| Bumper cars | 35c |
| Water log splash | 65c |
| Mini roller coaster | 80c |
| Bouncy castle | 25c |
| Trampoline | 55c |
| Ghost train | 40c |
| Water slide | 70c |

Total Marks: | /22 | Got this!  Getting there.  Need help!

I loved doing

# 15 🐕 Weight

**We are learning to:** Compare and sort weights into lighter than or heavier than. ☐
Investigate weight using non-standard and standard units of measurement. ☐

**Day One** Look at the example below.

Ann and Cory have identical buckets. Ann fills half of her bucket with sand and Cory fills his whole bucket with sand. Who has the heavier weight?

**CLUES**

**C**ircle the numbers and keywords:
identical bucket, fills half, fills whole, heavier

**L**ink with operation needed (+ or −): None

**U**se a strategy: Draw a picture.

**E**stimate and calculate:
My estimate: Using identical buckets, the full bucket must be heavier than the half-full bucket.

**Answer:**
Cory

**S**ummarise how you got your answer:
I drew a picture of a full bucket of sand and a half-full bucket of sand and saw that the full bucket was the heavier weight.

**Top Tip!**
Use the same weight container when comparing weights.

**Try these.**

**CLUES**

(1) Would a lunch box filled with marshmallows be **heavier** or **lighter** than a lunch box filled with cherry tomatoes?

Answer: | Marks: | /1

(2) If it takes **5** grapes to balance **1** plum, how many grapes do I need to balance **3** plums?

Answer: | Marks: | /2

(3) There are **30** dishwasher tablets in a $\frac{1}{2}$ kg box. How many dishwasher tablets are there in a 1 kg box?

Answer: | Marks: | /1

Strand: Measures Strand Unit: Weight

**Today's Marks:** | /4

## Day Two Try these.

**C**LUE**s**

**1** If there are **12** cubes on one side of a weighing scales and **27** on the other side, how many **less** do I need to balance the scales?

Answer: [ ] Marks: [ ] /1

**2** If it takes **4** sliotars to balance **1** soccer ball, how many sliotars do I need to balance **3** soccer balls?

Answer: [ ] Marks: [ ] /2

**3** If a pair of shorts weighs $\frac{1}{2}$ as much as a pair of jeans, how many pairs of jeans do I need to balance **8** pairs of shorts?

Answer: [ ] Marks: [ ] /2

## Super Sleuth challenge

| Rice | Crackers | Strawberries | Butter |
|---|---|---|---|
| 1 kg | $\frac{1}{4}$ kg | $\frac{1}{4}$ kg | $\frac{1}{2}$ kg |

| Cheese | Mince | Tomatoes | Potatoes |
|---|---|---|---|
| $\frac{1}{4}$ kg | $\frac{1}{2}$ kg | $\frac{1}{4}$ kg | 1 kg |

**Team Talk**

Reader
Calculator
Checker
Reporter

1. Which **4** items could you use to balance the weight of the potatoes?

2. Which item could you put with the tomatoes and strawberries to balance the weight of the rice?

3. Can you think of any questions based on the weights above?

Today's Marks: [ ] /5

65

### Day Three  Try these.

**1** **1** bag of flour weighs the same as **5** packets of biscuits. How many packets of biscuits do I need to balance **2** bags of flour?

| Answer: | | Marks: | | /1 |

**2** Derek's mum is making pizzas. To make **1** pizza, she needs $\frac{1}{4}$ kg of flour. How many quarters of a kilogram of flour will she need to make **3** pizzas?

**Top Tip!**
Draw a picture.

| Answer: | | Marks: | | /1 |

**3** It takes **16** cubes to balance **1** copy and **2** pencils. If it takes **3** cubes to balance **1** pencil, how many cubes do I need to balance just the copy?

| Answer: | | Marks: | | /2 |

**4** You work in the post office and you need to calculate the weight of 6 parcels for a customer. Use the table to help you work out the total weight of the following:

- **1** parcel weighing 1 kg
- **3** parcels weighing $\frac{1}{2}$ kg each
- **2** parcels weighing $\frac{1}{4}$ kg each

| Weight | Number of parcels | Weight |
|---|---|---|
| 1 kg | | |
| $\frac{1}{2}$ kg | | |
| $\frac{1}{4}$ kg | | |
| **Total weight:** | | |

| Answer: | | Marks: | | /3 |

Today's Marks: | | /7

## Day Four  Try these.

Jodie went to Thrifty Market to buy some onions and tomatoes. Look at their cost and answer the questions below.

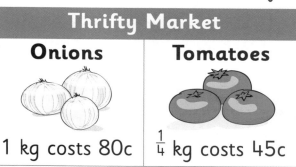

**Thrifty Market**

| Onions | Tomatoes |
|---|---|
| 1 kg costs 80c | $\frac{1}{4}$ kg costs 45c |

**(1)** How much would Jodie pay for 1 kg of onions and $\frac{1}{4}$ kg of tomatoes?

**Top Tip!**
Make a table.

Answer: €            Marks:        /1

**(2)** How much would Jodie pay for $\frac{1}{2}$ kg of onions and $\frac{1}{2}$ kg of tomatoes?

Answer: €            Marks:        /1

**(3)** How much would Jodie pay for 1 kg of onions and $\frac{1}{2}$ kg of tomatoes?

Answer: €            Marks:        /1

**(4) (a)** How much would Jodie pay for $\frac{1}{4}$ kg of onions and $\frac{1}{2}$ kg of tomatoes? **(b)** How much change would she get from €2?

Answers: (a) €            (b) €            Marks:        /2

Today's Marks:        /5

Total Marks:        /21      Got this!  ⬤  Getting there.  ⬤  Need help!  ⬤

I would like to get better at

# 16 Time 1

## Day One — Look at the example below.

Hurling training started at 5 o'clock and lasted for 1 hour. At what time did it finish?

**CLUES**

**C**ircle the numbers and keywords:
   5 o'clock, lasted for 1 hour, finish

**L**ink with operation needed (+ or −): Add (+).

**U**se a strategy: Act it out.

**E**stimate and calculate: | 5 + 1 = 6 | **Answer:** 6 o'clock

**S**ummarise how you got your answer: I added 5 + 1.

**Try these.**

**CLUES**

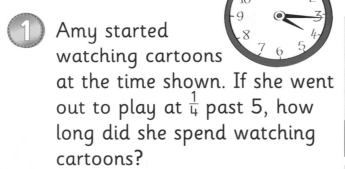

**1** Amy started watching cartoons at the time shown. If she went out to play at $\frac{1}{4}$ past 5, how long did she spend watching cartoons?

Answer: _____  Marks: ___ /1

**2** Kay's piano lesson started at 5 o'clock. It finished at half past 5. For how long did the lesson last?

Answer: _____  Marks: ___ /1

**3** David had a doctor's appointment at 3 o'clock. He arrived $\frac{1}{2}$ an hour early. At what time did he arrive?

Answer: _____  Marks: ___ /1

**Today's Marks:** _____ /3

**Day Two** Try these.

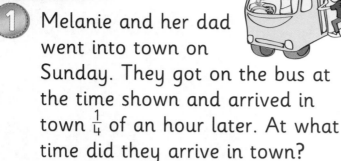

**1** Melanie and her dad went into town on Sunday. They got on the bus at the time shown and arrived in town $\frac{1}{4}$ of an hour later. At what time did they arrive in town?

Answer: [ ] Marks: [ ] /1

**2** Darragh leaves for school at the time shown. It takes him $\frac{1}{2}$ an hour to walk to school and he has $\frac{1}{4}$ of an hour of playtime in the yard before school starts. At what time does school start?

**Top Tip!**
Act it out using a clock face.

Answer: [ ] Marks: [ ] /1

**3** Evie left her house at the time shown. It took her $\frac{1}{4}$ of an hour to walk to her friend Julie's house, where she played for 2 hours. At what time did Evie leave Julie's house?

Answer: [ ] Marks: [ ] /2

**4** Look at the TV guide.

**(a)** It is half past 9 now. For how long does Tara have to wait until *Dora the Explorer* starts?
**(b)** For how long are both *Back at the Barnyard* and *Skunk Fu!* on?

| 9:30 | Paw Patrol |
|------|-----------|
| 10:00 | Dora the Explorer |
| 10:30 | Olive the Ostrich |
| 11:00 | Back at the Barnyard |
| 11:30 | Skunk Fu! |
| 12:00 | Wipeout |

Answers: (a) [ ] (b) [ ] Marks: [ ] /2

Today's Marks: [ ] /6

**Day Three** Try these.

CLUEs

1 Eric's alarm went off at 7:00. He pressed the snooze button and the alarm went off again at 7:30. How many minutes later was this?

Answer: ___ Marks: ___ /1

2 Sally looked at her digital watch and saw that it was 9:30. Maths had started 30 minutes earlier. In digital time, at what time did maths start?

Answer: ___ Marks: ___ /1

3 Kieran's birthday party started at 3:30 and lasted for 2 and a half hours. In digital time, at what time did the party end?

Answer: ___ Marks: ___ /2

4 Ralph finished his homework at 4:00. He had spent $\frac{1}{4}$ of an hour on English and $\frac{1}{4}$ of an hour on maths. In digital time, at what time did he start doing his homework?

Answer: ___ Marks: ___ /2

**Puzzle power**

What kind of songs do aliens like to sing?

| 12 o'clock = E | $\frac{1}{2}$ past 6 = N |
|---|---|
| $\frac{1}{2}$ past 10 = U | 1 o'clock = S |
| 7 o'clock = T | $\frac{1}{2}$ past 3 = P |

| 6:30 | 12:00 | 3:30 | 7:00 | 10:30 | 6:30 | 12:00 | 1:00 |
|---|---|---|---|---|---|---|---|
| | | | | | | | |

Today's Marks: ___ /6

## Day Four  Try these.

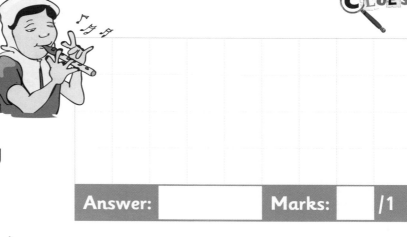

**1** Aisha spent a quarter of an hour practising the tin whistle on Monday, Tuesday and Wednesday. How many minutes did she spend practising altogether?

Answer: ⬚  Marks: ⬚ /1

**2** Gearóid's mum has a hair appointment at 11 o'clock. It will take her half an hour to drive to the hair salon. In digital time, at what time will she need to leave home?

Answer: ⬚  Marks: ⬚ /1

**3** A match kicked off at 5:00. Half-time began at a quarter to 6 and lasted for a quarter of an hour. The second half of the match lasted for 45 minutes. At what time did the match end?

Answer: ⬚  Marks: ⬚ /3

Today's Marks: ⬚ /5

## Super Sleuth investigates

At 12 o'clock, the small hand and the big hand are both pointing in the same direction. At what other times are the small hand and the big hand both pointing in the same direction?

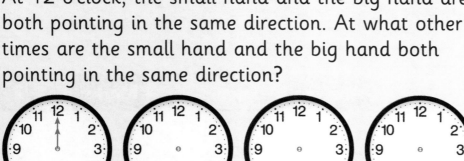

**Team Talk**

Reader

Calculator

Checker

Reporter

Total Marks: ⬚ /20   Got this!  ⬤  Getting there.  ⬤  Need help!  ⬤

I enjoyed

71

# 17 Data

**We are learning to:** Sort and classify objects by two and three criteria. ☐
Understand how to represent, read and interpret pictograms and block graphs. ☐

## Day One Look at the example below.

The pupils in Jane's class voted for their favourite computer game. This pictogram shows the results. How many pupils are there in Jane's class?

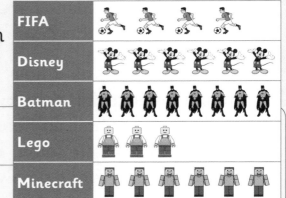

| FIFA | |
| Disney | |
| Batman | |
| Lego | |
| Minecraft | |

**C**LUES

**C**ircle the numbers and keywords: how many pupils?

**L**ink with operation needed (+ or −): Add (+).

**U**se a strategy: Act it out.

**E**stimate and calculate:
Add the pictures: 4 + 6 + 8 + 3 + 6 = 27

**Answer:**
27 pupils

**S**ummarise how you got your answer:
I added the pictures in the pictogram.

Try these.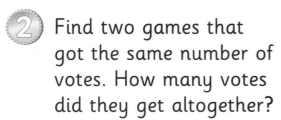

1. Look at the pictogram above. Find the game that got the most votes. How many votes did it get?

**Answer:** **Marks:** /2

2. Find two games that got the same number of votes. How many votes did they get altogether?

**Answer:** **Marks:** /2

3. Only 3 girls voted for the FIFA and Lego games in total. How many boys voted for these games?

**Answer:** **Marks:** /2

Strand: Data Strand Unit: Representing and Interpreting Data

**Today's Marks:** /6

## Day Two  Try these.

During the month of September, Darren's class recorded the weather at 12 o'clock every school day. They did this by drawing the following weather symbols on the calendar:

for sunny      for cloudy      for raining

| Mon | Tues | Wed | Thurs | Fri | Sat | Sun |
|------|------|------|------|------|------|------|
|  | 1 ☀ | 2 ☁ | 3 ☀ | 4 🌧 | 5 | 6 |
| 7 ☀ | 8 ☁ | 9 🌧 | 10 ☀ | 11 ☀ | 12 | 13 |
| 14 ☁ | 15 ☀ | 16 ☀ | 17 ☁ | 18 🌧 | 19 | 20 |
| 21 ☁ | 22 🌧 | 23 ☀ | 24 🌧 | 25 ☁ | 26 | 27 |
| 28 ☁ | 29 ☀ | 30 ☀ |  |  |  |  |

**1** Fill in the pictogram using the data in the calendar above. Do your best drawing the symbols!

| Sunny days | |
|---|---|
| **Cloudy days** | |
| **Rainy days** | |

Marks: /3

**2** On the days that it rained, the pupils had to stay indoors for their lunch break. On how many school days could they **not** go outside and play?

Answer: _____  Marks: /1

**3** Which week had the least amount of sunny days? Write the date on which this week began.

Answer: _____  Marks: /1

**4** If it rained on **3** weekend days and was cloudy on **2** weekend days, on how many weekend days was it sunny?

Answer: _____  Marks: /2

**Day Three** Try these.

Ava's class were asked to vote for their favourite board games. This was how they voted:

| Chess | Connect 4 | Guess Who? | Monopoly | Draughts | Scrabble |
|-------|-----------|------------|----------|----------|----------|
| 3 | 5 | 2 | 10 | 3 | 7 |

1 **(a)** Draw the blocks on the block graph below to show the votes for each board game. Use a ruler to help you draw the blocks.

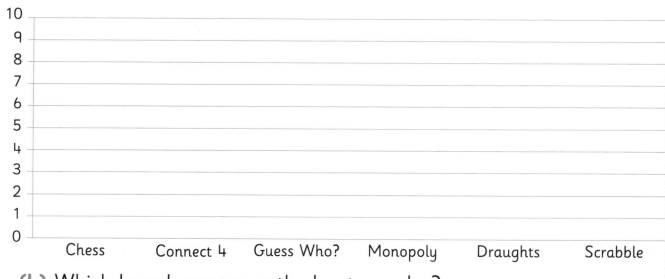

**(b)** Which board game was the least popular?

Answer: (b)          Marks:   /7

2 How many fewer pupils voted for chess **and** Guess Who than Scrabble?

Answer:    Marks:   /1

3 How many pupils are there in Ava's class altogether?

Answer:    Marks:   /2

4 Which 2 games together got half of the class votes?

Answer:        Marks:   /2

Today's Marks:   /12

**Day Four** **Try these.**

There are **28** boys and girls in a class. They were asked what their favourite activities were. Here is a block graph showing the results:

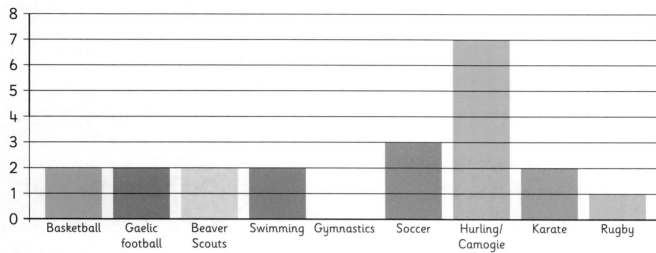

1  If **half** of the total votes for basketball, Beaver Scouts and karate were made by boys, how many boys voted for these activities?

Answer: ____  Marks: ____ /2

2  If 3 girls voted for Gaelic football, swimming and soccer, how many boys voted for these activities?

Answer: ____  Marks: ____ /2

3  The gymnastics value was not drawn in. Work out how many pupils voted for gymnastics and then draw the block.

Answer: ____  Marks: ____ /3

Today's Marks: ____ /7

Total Marks: ____ /32   Got this!  ◯  Getting there.  ◯  Need help!  ◯

My favourite activity was _____

# 18 Revision 3

## Saturday in Castle Town

### Day One Try these.

**(1)** At the Castle Town Bookshop, Tanya used three coins to pay exactly **72c** for a comic. Which three coins did she pay with?

Marks: /3

**(2)** Tony bought **6** Match Attax cards costing **15c** each. How much did he pay?

**Top Tip!**
Identify a pattern.

Answer: _____ Marks: /1

**(3)** Dean bought a pen for **46c** and a rubber for **37c**. How much change did he get from the coins shown?

Answer: _____ Marks: /2

**(4)** Bríd and Maura went to the bookshop café for a snack.

**(a)** Bríd bought a cup of tea and a cream bun. How much change did she get from **€2**?

**(b)** Maura bought a carton of juice and a cookie. How much change did she get from **€2**?

**PRICE LIST**
Tea or coffee 90c
Carton of juice 50c
Cream bun 60c
Cookie 20c

Answers: (a) _____ (b) € _____ Marks: /4

**Strand:** Measures **Strand Units:** Money; Weight; Time
**Strand:** Data **Strand Unit:** Representing and Interpreting Data

**Today's Marks:** /10

**Day Two** Try these.

C LUE's

1. At Luigi and Maria's Italian Diner, Luigi baked a chocolate pie that weighed 1 kg. Maria baked a lemon pie that weighed $\frac{1}{2}$ kg less than Luigi's. Who baked the heavier pie?

Answer:     Marks:   /1

2. Luigi and Maria can feed **4** customers with one packet of pasta weighing $\frac{1}{2}$ kg. On Saturday, **8** customers ordered pasta. How many packets of pasta did Luigi and Maria cook?

Answer:     Marks:   /1

3. If **16** customers ordered pasta on Saturday night, how many packets of pasta did Luigi and Maria cook then?

Answer:     Marks:   /2

4. Maria went out to the pet shop to buy cans of food for her two dogs. Buster eats $\frac{1}{4}$ kg of dog food **twice** a day. Doris eats $\frac{1}{4}$ kg of dog food **once** a day. For how many days would a 1 kg tin of dog food last **(a)** Buster and **(b)** Doris?

Buster

Doris

CHUM

Answers: (a)     (b)     Marks:   /2

Today's Marks:   /6

**Day Three** Try these.

1) At Castle Town Library, a puppet show started at a quarter to 12 and finished at a quarter past 12. For how long did it last?

Answer: ___ Marks: ___ /1

2) Kids' Story Club started at half past 2. Katie the librarian read a ghost story for $\frac{1}{4}$ of an hour, a fairytale for $\frac{1}{4}$ of an hour and a story set in outer space for $\frac{1}{4}$ of an hour. At what time did she finish?

Answer: ___ Marks: ___ /2

3) Junior Poets' Club started at 4:00 and lasted for half an hour. When it ended, Katie took a coffee break that lasted for $\frac{1}{4}$ of an hour. At what time did she finish her coffee break?

Answer: ___ Marks: ___ /2

4) Dylan and his dad went to the library to watch a film about Vikings. It started at 3:30 and lasted for 1 and a half hours. The drive home took half an hour. In digital time, at what time did they arrive home?

Answer: ___ Marks: ___ /2

Today's Marks: ___ /7

## Day Four  Try these.

A Saturday soccer tournament was held at Castle Town Park. The pictogram below shows the number of goals scored.

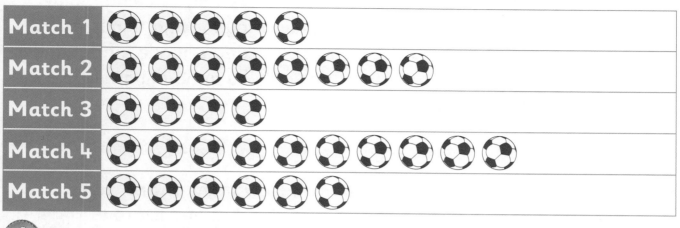

1. How many goals altogether were scored in the first two matches?

Answer: ____    Marks: ____ /1

2. Niamh scored half of the goals in the second-last match. How many goals did she score?

Answer: ____    Marks: ____ /2

3. How many **more** goals were scored in the last two matches than in the first two matches?

Answer: ____    Marks: ____ /3

4. If **double** the number of goals was scored at the previous Saturday tournament, how many goals were scored that day?

Answer: ____    Marks: ____ /3

Today's Marks: ____ /9

# 19 🕵️ Strategy: Make a Model

## Day One

We all learn in different ways. Some people learn by listening. Some people learn by watching. Some people learn by making things, such as constructing a shape with Lego bricks. Making a model of a number story can help you to work it out more easily by using things like bricks, cubes, lollipop sticks and counters.

**Try these.**

**1** Grainne arranged 4 cubes as shown. How many **more** cubes does she need to make a square with 3 cubes in each row?

Answer: ☐  Marks: ☐ /1

**2** Alfie is making a board for a board game using black and white blocks. He has started the first two rows as shown. How many more **(a)** black cubes and **(b)** white cubes does he need to complete his board?

Answers (a): ☐
(b): ☐  Marks: ☐ /2

**3** Look at the building blocks. By changing the order of the blocks, how many different ways could you stack them?

Answer: ☐  Marks: ☐ /3

Today's Marks: ☐ /6

## Day Two Try these.

**1** Bob the Builder is building a winners' podium for race day. He uses six blocks to build steps for 1st, 2nd and 3rd places. How many **more** blocks would he need to build a step for 4th place?

Answer: ☐ Marks: ☐ /1

**2** At the end of the day, Bob likes to arrange bricks in stacks of equal height. He can only take 1 or 2 bricks from each stack at a time, because they are so heavy. How can he make the stacks equal in just **two** moves?

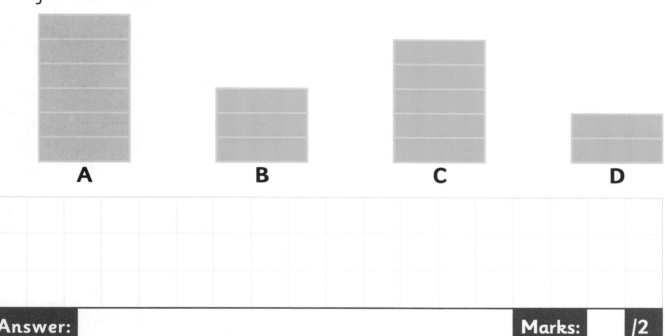

A　　　　B　　　　C　　　　D

Answer: ☐ Marks: ☐ /2

**3** **(a)** Estimate how many small cubes are in a Rubik's Cube altogether. **(b)** Use cubes to make a Rubik's Cube like the one shown. Were you near your estimate?

Answers: (a) ☐ (b) ☐ Marks: ☐ /2

Today's Marks: ☐ /5　**81**

## Day Three  Try these.

**1** Look at the image. The artist got the sum wrong! Can you move just **one** matchstick to correct the sum? Try making a model using matchsticks.

6 + 5 = 9

Marks: /1

**2** Using unifix cubes, make a few models of shapes A and B below. How could you arrange these shapes on the grid so that they fit together and cover the entire grid? How many of **(a)** shape A and **(b)** shape B would you need?

**Shape A**      **Shape B**      **Grid**

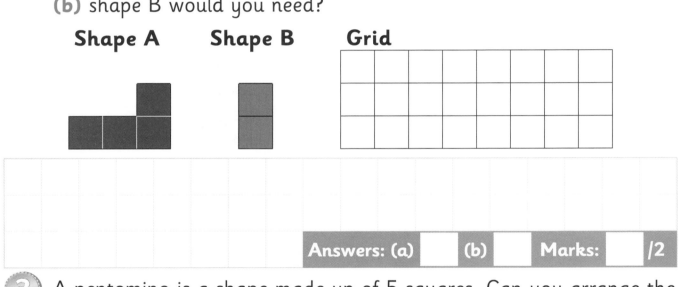

Answers: (a) ☐ (b) ☐  Marks: ☐ /2

**3** A pentomino is a shape made up of 5 squares. Can you arrange the pentominoes below in the grid so that thay fit together like a jigsaw puzzle? Make models of the pentominoes using unifix cubes first.

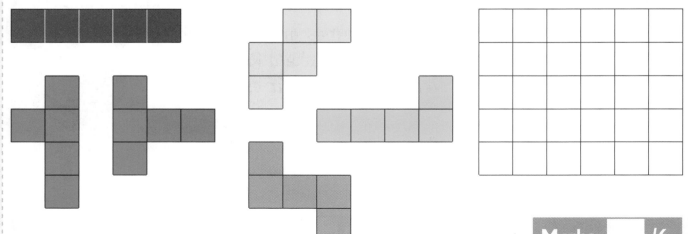

Marks: /6

Today's Marks: /9

## Day Four  Try these.

C(LUE)s

**1** Henry uses 6 playing cards to make the bottom row of a **triangular** tower. He places 2 cards flat on top of this row. How many cards will he need to make the next two rows up?

Answer: [ ]   Marks: [ ] /2

**2** You have 12 counters. Place them in the grid so that there are only 3 counters in each row (across) and column (down). (Hint: You can leave some squares blank.)

● ● ● ● ● ● ● ● ● ● ● ●

= 3
= 3
= 3
= 3

Marks: [ ] /2

= 3   = 3   = 3   = 3

**3** Image A shows 2 cubes joined together. Image B shows 1 cube made with cocktail sticks and mini marshmallows. How many cocktail sticks would you need to make 2 cubes joined together similar to image A?

**A**          **B**

Answer: [ ]   Marks: [ ] /2

Today's Marks: [ ] /6

## Puzzle power ✏

Look at the image. By moving only one glass, how could you arrange it so that the glasses have a pattern of full, empty, full, empty, full, empty, in that order?

Total Marks: [ ] /26   Got this! 👍⚪   Getting there. ✊⚪   Need help! 👎⚪

I helped my friend by [ ]

# 20 Symmetry

We are learning to: Identify line symmetry in shapes and in the environment. ☐

**Day One** Look at the example below.

Where could you draw a line and fold this shape so that it will fold over exactly onto itself?

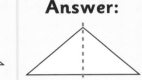

**C**ircle the numbers and keywords:
  shape, fold over exactly onto itself

**L**ink with operation needed (+ or −): None

**U**se a strategy: Make a model. Draw the shape. Cut it out and try folding it exactly in half.

**E**stimate and calculate:
  It folds exactly here. ——→
  This is a line of symmetry.

**Answer:**

**S**ummarise how you got your answer:
  I used my ruler to draw a line where the shape folded over exactly onto itself.

Try these.

① Draw the line of symmetry in each of the shapes below.

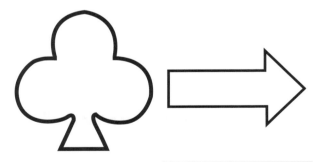

Marks: ☐ /2

② Draw the other half of the bun to make it symmetrical.

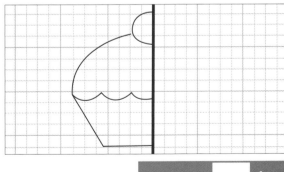

Marks: ☐ /2

③ Colour the squares to the right of the red line to make the grid symmetrical.

Marks: ☐ /2

Today's Marks: ☐ /6

**Day Two** Try these.

1 Draw the line of symmetry in the racing car.

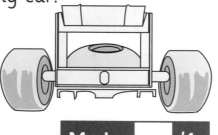

Marks: ☐ /1

2 Draw one line of symmetry in each of the digits below.

0   3   8

Marks: ☐ /3

3 Finish this symmetrical pattern below the red line.

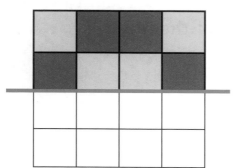

Marks: ☐ /2

4 Colour the black squares to the right of the red line so that the butterfly is symmetrical.

**Top Tip!**

Work with a pencil at first, so that you can correct any mistakes.

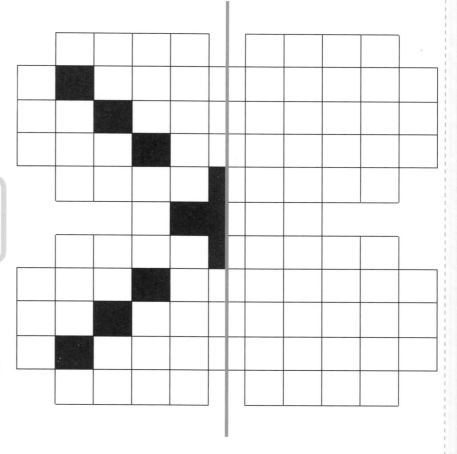

Choose your own colours to colour the rest of the squares in a symmetrical pattern.

Marks: ☐ /3

Today's Marks: ☐ /9

85

**Day Three** Try these.

1 Draw one line of symmetry in each of the capital letters below.

# B O O K

Marks: ☐ /4

2 Ring the shape below that has **no** line of symmetry.

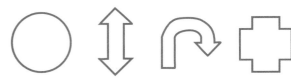

Marks: ☐ /1

3 Draw a design of colourful squares and rectangles to the left of the red line. Swap with a partner and ask them to draw the mirror image of your design to the right of the red line.

Answer: ☐        Marks: ☐ /2

4 Draw the other half of the picture so that it is symmetrical.

Answer: ☐        Marks: ☐ /3

Today's Marks: ☐ /10

**Day Four** Try these.

**1** Draw two lines of symmetry in the snowflake.

Marks: ☐ /2

**2** Ring the capital letters below that have **no** line of symmetry.

# C N H P

Marks: ☐ /2

**3** Draw the other half of the owl.

Marks: ☐ /2

**4** Draw black dots in the grid to the **left** of the blue line to make the two sides symmetrical. Then, draw black dots **below** the red line to make the top and bottom parts symmetrical.

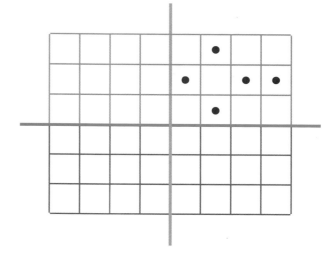

Marks: ☐ /3

Today's Marks: ☐ /9

Total Marks: ☐ /34

Got this!  ◯ Getting there.  ◯ Need help!  ◯

I loved doing _____

# 21  Angles

**We are learning to:** Explore and recognise angles in the environment. ☐

**Day One** Look at the example below.

Mum wants to heat up beans. She has to turn the knob on the cooker to number 2. Will the knob make a full turn, a half turn or a quarter turn?

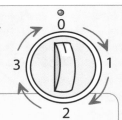

**C**LUEs

**C**ircle the numbers and keywords:

a full turn, a half turn or a quarter turn?

**L**ink with operation needed (+ or −): None

**U**se a strategy: Act it out with a circle and a lollipop stick.

**E**stimate and calculate:

This is a half turn, because it goes half-way around.

**Answer:**
a half turn

**S**ummarise how you got your answer: I acted it out.

Try these.

**C**LUEs

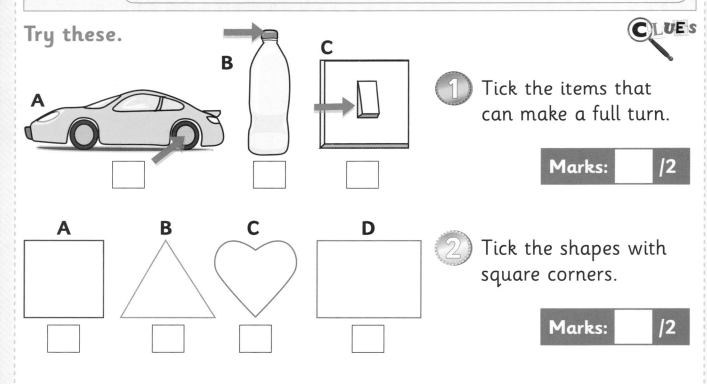

A

B

C

① Tick the items that can make a full turn.

**Marks:** ☐ /2

A B C D

② Tick the shapes with square corners.

**Marks:** ☐ /2

③  Write three other times at which the hands on a clock make a square corner.

**Answer:** ☐ **Marks:** ☐ /4

Strand: Shape and Space Strand Unit: Angles

**Today's Marks:** ☐ /8

**Day Two** Try these.

**1** How many square corners are there in this picture frame?

**Answer:** ☐ **Marks:** ☐ **/1**

**2** **(a)** Seán wants to change this picture of a hot-air balloon on his computer.

**(b)** If he clicks on the rotate button **once**, the picture will make a **quarter turn** to the **right**.

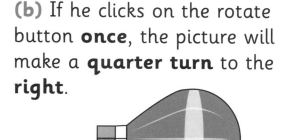

**(c)** Draw how the balloon will look if he clicks on the rotate button **twice**.

**(d)** Draw how the balloon will look if he clicks on the rotate button **three times.**

**Marks:** ☐ **/2**

**3** In image A below, Hannah is standing on a roundabout in the playground. This roundabout turns to the **right**. If the roundabout makes a **full turn** plus a **quarter turn**, where will Hannah be standing in image B? Mark the spot with an 'X'.

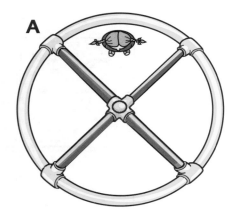

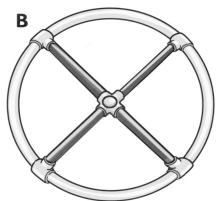

**Marks:** ☐ **/1**

**Today's Marks:** ☐ **/4**

**Day Three** Try these.

1 When you are walking upstairs, how many square corners can you count on each stair?

Answer: [ ] Marks: [ ] /1

2 The image below shows a revolving (rotating) door at the front of a hotel. The door turns to the right. Greg is leaving the hotel. What type of turn must the door make for Greg to get outside: a **half** turn, a **quarter** turn or a **full** turn?

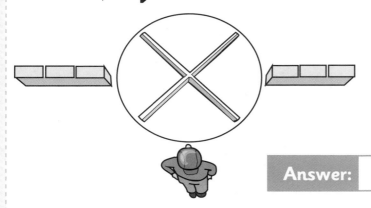

**Top Tip!**
Jump into the page and imagine that you are there!

Answer: [ ] Marks: [ ] /1

3 This game show wheel turns to the right. **(a)** If it makes a **half turn**, which number will end up at the pointer? **(b)** If it **then** makes a **quarter turn**, which number will end up at the pointer?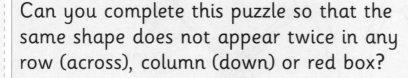

**Top Tip!**
Draw a diagram showing the answer to question (a) and use this to help you answer question (b).

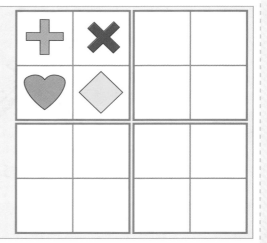

Answers: (a) [ ] (b) [ ] Marks: [ ] /2

**Puzzle Power** ✏️

Can you complete this puzzle so that the same shape does not appear twice in any row (across), column (down) or red box?

| ＋ | ✖ | | |
|---|---|---|---|
| ♥ | ◇ | | |
| | | | |
| | | | |

Today's Marks: [ ] /4

## Day Four  Try these.

**1** How many square corners can you count in these two capital letters?

# H E

Answer: [        ] Marks: [    ] /1

**2** How many square corners can you see in this image?

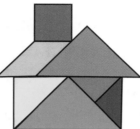

Answer: [        ] Marks: [    ] /1

**3** Using only **two** lollipop sticks each time, draw a diagram showing how you would make the following:

**(a)** 1 square corner

**(b)** 2 square corners

**(c)** 4 square corners

Marks: [    ] /3

Today's Marks: [    ] /5

## Super Sleuth investigates

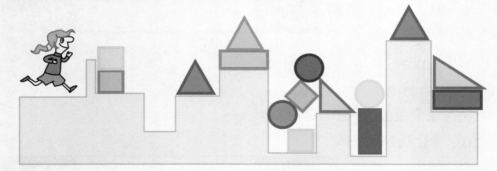

Helen is playing a computer game. She has to collect shapes with square corners only.

1. How many shapes have only one square corner?

2. How many shapes have more than one square corner?

Total Marks: [        ] /21

Got this!  ◯  Getting there.  ◯  Need help!  ◯

I would like to get better at [                                                  ]

**91**

# 22  Time 2

**We are learning to:** Read days, dates and months using a calendar and identify the season. ☐

---

**Day One** Look at the example below.

On Monday, Cian's mum tells him that he has a dental check-up in 3 days' time. On what day will Cian be going to the dentist?

**CLUEs**

**C**ircle the numbers and keywords: Monday, 3 days' time

**L**ink with operation needed (+ or –): None

**U**se a strategy: Draw a picture.

**E**stimate and calculate:

Count on 3 days from Monday.

| Mon | Tues | Wed | Thurs | Fri | Sat | Sun |
|-----|------|-----|-------|-----|-----|-----|

**Answer:**
Thursday

**S**ummarise how you got your answer:
I started at Monday and counted on 3 days.

---

**Try these.** **CLUEs**

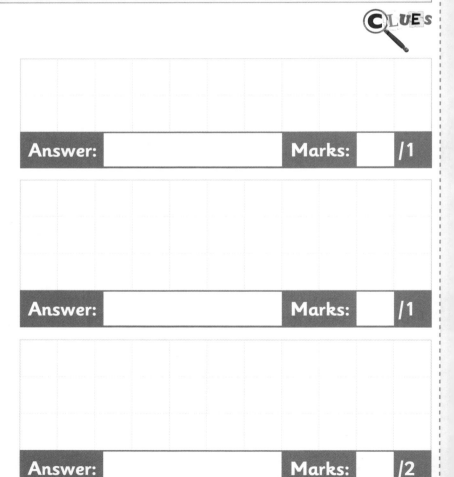

1 Kayla visited her granny **4** days **before** Tuesday. On what day did she visit her granny?

**Answer:** _____ **Marks:** ____ /1

2 Keegan will take part in a swimming competition **21** days from today. How many weeks away is this?

**Answer:** _____ **Marks:** ____ /1

3 What day and date will it be **21** days from today?

**Answer:** _____ **Marks:** ____ /2

Strand: Measures Strand Unit: Time

**Today's Marks:** ____ /4

## Day Two Try these.

**1** Matt's birthday is in March and Lucy's birthday is in August. How many months are there between their birthdays?

Answer: _____ Marks: ___ /1

**2** How many days are there in summer altogether?

Answer: _____ Marks: ___ /2

**Rhyme**

30 days have September, April, June and November. All the rest have 31, except for February alone, which has 28 days clear and 29 in each leap year.

**3** Look at the calendar months and answer the questions below.

| January | | | | | | |
|---|---|---|---|---|---|---|
| Mon | Tues | Wed | Thurs | Fri | Sat | Sun |
| | | | 1 | 2 | 3 | 4 |
| 5 | 6 | 7 | 8 | 9 | 10 | 11 |
| 12 | 13 | 14 | 15 | 16 | 17 | 18 |
| 19 | 20 | 21 | 22 | 23 | 24 | 25 |
| 26 | 27 | 28 | 29 | 30 | 31 | |

| February | | | | | | |
|---|---|---|---|---|---|---|
| Mon | Tues | Wed | Thurs | Fri | Sat | Sun |
| | | | | | | 1 |
| 2 | 3 | 4 | 5 | 6 | 7 | 8 |
| 9 | 10 | 11 | 12 | 13 | 14 | 15 |
| 16 | 17 | 18 | 19 | 20 | 21 | 22 |
| 23 | 24 | 25 | 26 | 27 | 28 | |

**(a)** After the Christmas holidays, Holly's school opened on the first Monday in January. On what **date** did Holly go back to school?

**(b)** Andy's guitar classes started on January 8th. What **day** was this?

**(c)** Andy went to the doctor on January 30th. The doctor told him to come back in 7 days' time. On what **date** did he go back to the doctor?

**(d)** On what **day** will March 1st fall?

Answers: (a) _____ (b) _____

(c) _____ (d) _____ Marks: ___ /4

## Day Three  Try these.

**1** The longest day of the year is June 21st.
The shortest day of the year is December 21st.
How many months are there between these
two dates?

**Top Tip!**
Identify patterns
in the calender
for the year.

Answer: _____ Marks: ___ /1

**2** Kathryn works as a nurse in a hospital. She sometimes
works at night. On Thursday night, she started work
at 8 o'clock. She finished at 8 o'clock the following
morning.

**(a)** What day was it when she finished work?

**(b)** How many hours did she work from her starting
time to finishing time?

Answers: (a) _____ (b) _____ Marks: ___ /2

**3** The All-Ireland Hurling Final
is usually held on the **first**
Sunday in September. The
GAA Football All-Ireland Final
is usually held on the **third**
Sunday in September.

| September | | | | | | |
|-----|------|-----|-------|-----|-----|-----|
| Mon | Tues | Wed | Thurs | Fri | Sat | Sun |
|     | 1    | 2   | 3     | 4   | 5   | 6   |
| 7   | 8    | 9   | 10    | 11  | 12  | 13  |
| 14  | 15   | 16  | 17    | 18  | 19  | 20  |
| 21  | 22   | 23  | 24    | 25  | 26  | 27  |
| 28  | 29   | 30  |       |     |     |     |

**(a)** Going by this calendar, on
what **date** will the All-Ireland Hurling Final final be held?

**(b)** Going by this calendar, on what **date** will the GAA Football
All-Ireland Final be held?

Answers: (a) _____ (b) _____ Marks: ___ /2

Today's Marks: ___ /5

**Day Four** Try these.

**C**LUE's

**1** Luke's eighth birthday is on January 29th. What age will he be **two years** from this date?

Answer: _____ Marks: ___ /1

**2** Megan's baby brother was born on November 5th. On what date of the following year will he be **7 months old**?

Answer: _____ Marks: ___ /2

**3** Tom gets paid for his job as a teacher every **2 weeks**. If he gets paid on April 4th, on what date will he next get paid?

Answer: _____ Marks: ___ /2

Today's Marks: ___ /5

**Puzzle power** ✏️ 💬

Choose a month of the year and then roll a die. Using the number rolled, count on and back by this number of months.

| Month | Number Rolled | + Answer | – Answer |
|---|---|---|---|
| February | 4 | June | October |
|  |  |  |  |
|  |  |  |  |
|  |  |  |  |
|  |  |  |  |

Total Marks: ___ /21  Got this!  ◯ Getting there.  ◯ Need help!  ◯

I enjoyed _____

# 23 Length

**We are learning to:** Select and use appropriate measuring instruments. ☐
Investigate length using standard units (metres and centimetres). ☐

## Day One  Look at the example below.

A snail can travel 2 cm in one minute.
How far can it travel in two minutes?

 **CLUES**

**C**ircle the numbers and keywords:
   2 cm in one minute, how far in two minutes?

**L**ink with operation needed (+ or –): None

**U**se a strategy: Identify a pattern – doubles.

**E**stimate and calculate:

| | | **Answer:** |
|---|---|---|
| My estimate: less than 10 | Double 2 is 4. | 4 cm |

**S**ummarise how you got your answer:
   I knew I had to double 2 to find two minutes' travel.

**Try these.**                    **CLUES**

1 Which of these would you use to measure the length of a rugby pitch: **(a)** a ruler, **(b)** a metre stick or **(c)** a trundle wheel?

| Answer: | Marks: | /1 |
|---|---|---|

2 Joe is **75 cm** in height. Omar is **4 cm taller** than Joe. What height is Omar?

| Answer: | Marks: | /1 |
|---|---|---|

3 Paul's tablet is **26 cm** in length. His mobile phone is **14 cm** in length. By how much is his tablet **longer** than his mobile phone?

| Answer: | Marks: | /1 |
|---|---|---|

Strand: Measures Strand Unit: Length

**Today's Marks:** /3

**Day Two** Try these.

Top Tip!

| 100 cm = 1 metre | 50 cm = $\frac{1}{2}$ metre | 25 cm = $\frac{1}{4}$ metre |

**1** Emily's markers are **14 cm** in length. Which of the following should she choose to store her markers? Tick the answer.

- A pencil case that is 10 cm in length
- A pencil case that is 18 cm in length
- A pencil case that is 50 cm in length

**Marks:** /1

**2** Alan is buying a new cooker. The cooker needs to fit into a space in his kitchen measuring **75 cm** in width. There also needs to be a **1 cm** gap on both sides of the cooker. Which of the following should he choose? Tick the answer.

- A cooker that is 73 cm in width
- A cooker that is 77 cm in width
- A cooker that is 79 cm in width

**Marks:** /1

**3** Jack's swing seat is **40 cm** from the ground. Jack has grown taller and his dad needs to raise the seat by a further **20 cm** from the ground. How far from the ground will the swing seat be then?

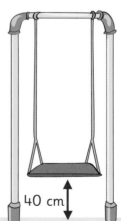

40 cm

**Answer:** **Marks:** /1

**4** Elaine is measuring her desk with lollipop sticks. One lollipop stick is **10 cm** long. If it takes 5 lollipop sticks to measure Elaine's desk from end to end, what fraction of a metre is this?

**Answer:** **Marks:** /2

**Today's Marks:** /5

97

### Day Three  Try these.

**1** The bar on Casey's scooter is **43 cm** long. The bar on Bryan's scooter is **54 cm** long. What is the **difference** between the bar lengths?

Answer: ___   Marks: ___ /1

**2** John is arranging a display of books on a shelf in a bookshop. Each book is **10 cm** in width. The shelf is **45 cm** in width. How many books can he display on the shelf?

Answer: ___   Marks: ___ /1

**3** Maisie is **78 cm** tall. She wants to reach the sink, but the sink is a height of **81 cm** from the floor. **(a)** What is the difference between Maisie's height and the height of the sink? **(b)** If Maisie stands on a stool that is **21 cm** in height, how far will the top of her head be from the floor?

**Team Talk**

Reader

Calculator

Checker

Reporter

Answers: (a) ___   (b) ___   Marks: ___ /2

### Puzzle power ✏

There is a 30 cm gap between each rung on Joe's ladder. Counting from the bottom rung up, how many rungs would Joe have to climb to be standing **over 1 metre** off the ground?

Today's Marks: ___ /4

## Day Four Try these.

**1** A blue penguin can grow up to **33 cm** in height. A rockhopper penguin can grow up to **55 cm** in height. What is the difference between these two heights?

**Top Tip!**
Draw a picture.

Answer: _____ Marks: [ ] /1

**2** You are asked to design a pencil case for an art competition. The pencil case needs to be **6 cm in length** and **2 cm in height**. Sketch your idea for the design in the box provided.

Marks: [ ] /2

**3** Bill's dad is hanging wallpaper on a wall in Bill's bedroom. The wall measures 3 metres in width. A strip of wallpaper measures $\frac{1}{2}$ metre in width. How many strips of wallpaper are needed to cover the wall?

Answer: _____ Marks: [ ] /3

## Puzzle power

Today's Marks: [ ] /6

If the beanstalk grows 5 cm in 1 minute, how many minutes will it take to grow to a height of $\frac{1}{2}$ metre?

**Total Marks:** [ ] /18   Got this!  ◯   Getting there.  ◯   Need help!  ◯

My favourite activity was _____

99

## Mega Monsters

**Day One** Try these.

1. Draw the line of symmetry in this monster's couch.

**Marks:** /1

2. Draw the other half of the monster to make it symmetrical.

**Marks:** /2

3. Draw the other half of the monster's den below the red line so that it is symmetrical.

**Marks:** /2

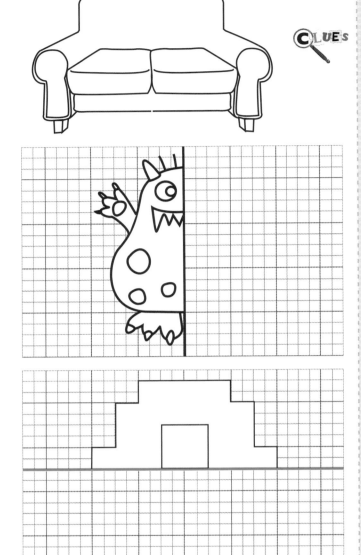

4. Identify two items in your classroom that are symmetrical. Draw and label them in the boxes below. Remember to draw the lines of symmetry.

(a)

(b)

**Marks:** /4

**Strand:** Shape and Space **Strand Units:** Symmetry; Angles
**Strand:** Measures **Strand Units:** Time; Length

**Today's Marks:** /9

## Day Two Try these.

**1** Oggy Ogre is ironing her woollen cloak and cotton dress for an important ogres' meeting. The dial on the iron turns to the right. Look at the dial. What type of turn does it make to **(a)** move from the **off** setting to the **wool** setting and **(b)** move from the **wool** setting to the **cotton** setting?

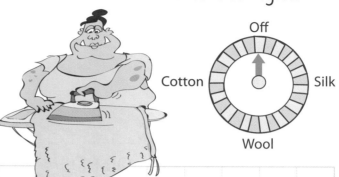

Answers: (a) _____ (b) _____ Marks: ____ /2

**2** This is the barrier outside the Ogres' Head Office. **(a)** What type of corner is marked on the image? **(b)** Can you find this corner anywhere else in this image? Mark it.

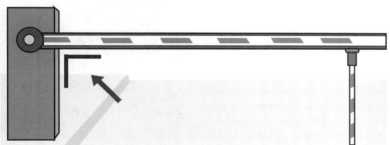

Answer: (a) _____

Marks: ____ /2

**3** Below is the flag of the Ogres' Head Office. **(a)** How many square corners can you find in the flag? **(b)** In the box provided, design a flag of your own that includes square corners.

Answer: (a) _____ Marks: ____ /3

## Day Three  Try these.

**1** Trevor Troll sowed a crop of daffodil bulbs in September. He had to wait 6 months for the delicious flowers to bloom. In which **season** did they bloom?

Answer: _____ Marks: ____ /1

**2** On Wednesday, Olaf Ogre ordered a present for his nephew from the Ogres' Head Office. The order arrived **4 working days later**, as there was no post on Saturday or Sunday. On what day of the following week did the order arrive?

Answer: _____ Marks: ____ /1

**3** Trudy Troll guards the troll bridge every second Thursday. If she works at the bridge on April 10th, on what date will she next be on duty?

| April | | | | | | |
|---|---|---|---|---|---|---|
| Mon | Tues | Wed | Thurs | Fri | Sat | Sun |
| | 1 | 2 | 3 | 4 | 5 | 6 |
| 7 | 8 | 9 | 10 | 11 | 12 | 13 |
| 14 | 15 | 16 | 17 | 18 | 19 | 20 |
| 21 | 22 | 23 | 24 | 25 | 26 | 27 |
| 28 | 29 | 30 | | | | |

Answer: _____ Marks: ____ /1

**4** Trenten Troll's 8th birthday was in March **this year**. Olga Ogre's 8th birthday was in November **last year**. **(a)** Is Olga older or younger than Trevor? **(b)** How many months are there between the two monsters' birthdays?

Answers: (a) _____ (b) _____ Marks: ____ /2

Today's Marks: ____ /5

## Day Four Try these.

**1** Clawbob Beast is measuring the length of his lunchbox. Should he use **(a)** a metre stick or **(b)** a 30 cm ruler?

Answer: [ ]   Marks: [ ] /1

**2** Clawdia Beast is hanging horrid artwork on a notice board in her cave. The notice board is **1 metre** in width. Each piece of artwork is **21 cm** in width. How many pieces of artwork can she place side by side on the notice board?

Answer: [ ]   Marks: [ ] /2

**3** Work out the **difference** between the length of Monstrous Mike's right foot and Snarling Sindy's right foot.

- Snarling Sindy's right foot is **21 cm** long.
- Rotten Ralph's right foot is 5 cm **shorter** than Snarling Sindy's.
- Monstrous Mike's right foot is 2 cm **longer** than Rotten Ralph's.

Answer: [ ]   Marks: [ ] /3

Today's Marks: [ ] /6

## Puzzle power

Follow the directions to see where Drooler is going in search of grub. (Hint: A fingernail is about 1 cm wide.)

- Go down 5 cm.
- Go right 4 cm.
- Go up 5 cm.
- Go left 1 cm.

Total Marks: [ ] /27

# 25  Strategy: Simplifying

## Day One

The word 'simplify' means to make something simpler or easier to understand. There are three ways to simplify a puzzle:

1. Reword the puzzle using a setting that you are familiar with.

2. Break it down into steps and solve it one part at a time.

3. Use smaller numbers at first, before going on to complete the puzzle with large numbers.

**Try these.**

**CLUEs**

1. Colette built a tower with Lego bricks. She started with 6 bricks on the bottom row and then used **2 fewer** bricks on each row until she ended up with 2 bricks on the top row. How many bricks did she use altogether?

← Bottom row

Answer: _____ Marks: ___ /1

2. List all of the **odd** numbers between 150 and 160.

Answer: _____

Marks: ___ /5

**Top Tip!**
Think of the odd numbers between 1 and 10. Then, think of those units in the bigger numbers.

3. Shane used 22 matchsticks to make squares joined together. How many squares did he make?

Answer: _____ Marks: ___ /1

Here are 2 squares joined together:

Today's Marks: ___ /7

**Day Two** Try these.

**C**LUE**s**

**1** At a New Year's Eve party, 4 friends gave each other a small present each. How many presents were exchanged in total?

Answer: Marks: /1

**2** Breda sells handmade mugs. Her shop is closed on Monday, Saturday and Sunday. Last week, she sold 30 mugs on Tuesday, 10 mugs on Wednesday and 30 mugs on Thursday. If she sold **90** mugs altogether last week, how many did she sell on Friday?

Answer: Marks: /2

**Top Tip!**
Try working with the numbers 3, 1, 3 and 9 at first.

**3** Tony is thinking of a mystery two-digit number. The number is **between** 20 and 30 and its **digits** add up to 7. Can you work out the number?

**Top Tip!**
Make a list of the pairs of units that add up to 7.

Answer: Marks: /1

**4** Using the numbers 10, 20, 30, 40, 50 and 60, arrange the numbers in the triangle so that each side adds up to **90**.

Marks: /6

**Day Three** Try these.

**1** The Walsh family are going on holidays. Each adult is bringing 1 large suitcase and 1 small bag. Each child is bringing only 1 small bag. There are **3** large suitcases and **7** small bags altogether.

**(a)** How many adults are going on holidays?

**(b)** How many children are going on holidays?

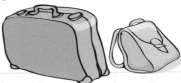

Answers: (a) ___ (b) ___ Marks: ___ /2

**2** Rex and his brother Rod each had **80c**. Rex spent $\frac{1}{2}$ of his amount. Rod found more money under the couch equalling $\frac{1}{2}$ of his amount. How much money do they have between them now?

**Top Tip!**
Think of yourself in this puzzle.

Answer: € ___ Marks: ___ /3

**3** Bobby sells bicycles and tricycles in his shop. He displays them in rows as follows: bicycle, tricycle, bicycle, tricycle and so on. There are 2 rows of bicycles and tricycles with an equal number of bicycles and tricycles in each row. He counts **40 wheels** in total.

**Team Talk**

Reader

Calculator

Checker

Reporter

**(a)** How many bicycles are there? **(b)** How many tricycles are there?

Answers: (a) ___ (b) ___ Marks: ___ /2

Today's Marks: ___ /7

**Day Four** Try these.

(C)LUEs

**1** Write out all of the numbers **between** 10 and 35 that have the digit **2**. (Hint: There are 12 numbers.)

Answer:

Marks: /12

**2** Miss Kelly drew three squares on the whiteboard. The first square had sides of **16 cm** in length. The **second** square had sides of **half** the length of the first square. The **third** square had sides of **half** the length of the second square. What was the length of each side in the third square?

Answer:

Marks: /2

**3** Bruce had 18 Match Attax cards. He put 6 of them in his album. He gave $\frac{1}{2}$ of what was left to his friend Jill and shared the rest equally between his friends Andy and Eugene. Later on, Bruce's dad gave him 3 packs of Match Attax cards with 6 cards in each pack.

**Team Talk**

Reader

Calculator

Checker

Reporter

**(a)** How many cards did Jill get? **(b)** How many cards did Andy and Eugene each get? **(c)** How many cards did Bruce have after his dad gave him the 3 packs?

Answers: (a) (b) (c) Marks: /3

Today's Marks: /17

Total Marks: /41 Got this!  Getting there. Need help!

I helped my friend by

# 26  3-D Shapes

**We are learning to:** Name, describe and compare 3-D shapes. ☐
Identify 3-D shapes in the environment. ☐
Understand the relationship between 2-D and 3-D shapes. ☐

## Day One  Look at the example below.

There are 12 edges on a cube. How many edges are there on 2 cubes?

**Top Tip!**
This is one edge.

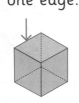

**C**ircle the numbers and keywords: 12 edges, 2 cubes

**L**ink with operation needed (+ or –): Add (+).

**U**se a strategy: Act it out.

**E**stimate and calculate:

My estimate:
double the number 12

| $12 + 12 = 24$ | **Answer:** 24 |

**S**ummarise how you got your answer:
12 edges on 1 cube, 24 edges on 2 cubes.

Try these.

1  How many **curved surfaces** are there on a disco ball?

Answer: [        ]  Marks: [    ] /1

2  How many **edges** are there altogether on two tins of beans?

Answer: [        ]  Marks: [    ] /1

3  Finn rolls two dice. After the dice stop rolling, how many square **faces** can be seen on the two dice?

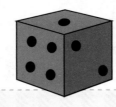

Answer: [        ]  Marks: [    ] /2

Today's Marks: [    ] /4

**Day Two** Try these.

CLUES

**1** Which of the following items are cylinders?

A B C D E

**Answer:** **Marks:** /3

**2** Sarah works at a pharmacy. She is stacking cuboid boxes containing bars of soap on a shelf. Each box is **6 cm** in height. When she has finished, the stack of boxes is **36** cm in height. How many boxes has she stacked?

Top Tip! Draw a picture.

**Answer:** **Marks:** /2

**3** Stephanie's dog had a litter of puppies. Stephanie needed to put cardboard on the floor in case the puppies had any 'accidents'! She got a cardboard box and opened it out. How many faces do you think there were on the cardboard box?

**Answer:** **Marks:** /2

## Super Sleuth challenge

Rob made a large cube using 9 small, white cubes. He painted the outside faces of his large cube red. When the paint dried, he broke up the large cube and placed all of the small cubes in a straight line. How many of the small cubes now had 3 red faces, 2 red faces and 1 red face?

Top Tip! Make a model.

**Team Talk**

Reader

Calculator

Checker

Reporter

**Day Three** Try these.

(1) During their art lesson, Noah's class dipped 3-D shapes into paint and used them to print squares and rectangles on paper. What 3-D shapes did they use?

**Top Tip!**
Make a model.

Answer: _____ Marks: ___ /2

(2) Lauren's teacher asked her to go over to the PE box and take out any balls that she could find for a game. Lauren found 2 soccer balls, 1 rugby ball, 6 tennis balls and 3 basketballs. How many spheres did Lauren find?

Answer: ___ Marks: ___ /1

(3) Jess works in a furniture shop. One day, she put 5 cone-shaped lamp shades side by side on a shelf. How many curved surfaces could she see on the 5 lamp shades?

Answer: ___ Marks: ___ /1

(4) Ryan's mum put some party food on the table for Ryan's birthday. There were **2** Swiss rolls, **6** walnut whips (cone shaped) and **1** cake in the shape of a soccer ball. How many **(a)** edges and **(b)** curved surfaces did the party food have altogether?

Answers: (a) ___ (b) ___ Marks: ___ /2

Today's Marks: ___ /6

**Day Four** Try these.

CLUEs

**1** There are a number of 3-D shapes in a bag. Altogether they have **10** faces. What shapes could be in the bag?

Answer:

Marks: /3

**2** Anna has **3** cubes and Evan has **4** cylinders. Who has more faces?

Answer:

Marks: /2

**3** Look at the image. How many **(a)** spheres, **(b)** cones and **(c)** cylinders can you find?

Answers: (a)

(b)

(c)

Marks: /3

**Super Sleuth investigates**

Today's Marks: /8

| Start → | | | Miss a turn | |
|---|---|---|---|---|
| Finish | | **The Great Shape Race!** | | |
| | | You will need a die and 2 counters. Roll the die and then move your counter. You score 1 point if you can name the 3-D shape that you land on. Take turns. Once both players have reached the finish line, the player with the highest score wins. | | **Go back two places** |
| Miss a turn | | | | |
| | | **Go back two places** | | |

**Total Marks:** /25

Got this! ○ Getting there. ○○ Need help! ○

I loved doing

111

# 27 Capacity

**We are learning to:** Investigate capacity using non-standard units. ☐
Measure capacity in litres, half-litres and quarter-litres. ☐

**Day One** Look at the example below.

It takes 2 spoons of yoghurt to fill 1 bowl. How many spoons of yoghurt are needed to fill 4 bowls?

**Keyword**

The **capacity** of a container is the amount of liquid that it can hold.

**C**ircle the numbers and keywords:
2 spoons to fill 1 bowl, fill 4 bowls

**L**ink with operation needed (+ or −): Add (+).

**U**se a strategy: Draw a picture.

**E**stimate and calculate:

2 + 2 + 2 + 2 = 8

**Answer:**
8

**S**ummarise how you got your answer:
I added 2 + 2 + 2 + 2 and got a total of 8.

Try these.

① Louise has to take **3** teaspoons of medicine every day for **4** days. How many teaspoons will she take in total?

Answer:     Marks:    /1

② Ian can fill **5** beakers of juice from 1 full carton. How many beakers could he fill from **3** full cartons?

Answer:     Marks:    /2

③ Last week, Puss in Boots drank **2** bowls of milk every day except for Friday, when he drank **3** bowls. How many bowls of milk did he drink last week?

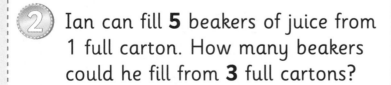

Answer:     Marks:    /2

Strand: Measures Strand Unit: Capacity

**Today's Marks:**    /5

## Day Two Try these.

Hannah's mum has asked her to buy **1 litre** of water at the supermarket.

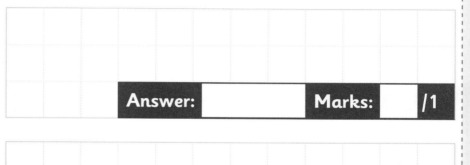

| The supermarket sells: | | |
| --- | --- | --- |
| **A** | **B** | **C** |
| $\frac{1}{4}$ litre bottle for 35c | $\frac{1}{2}$ litre bottle for 85c | 1 litre bottle for €1.60 |

1. How many $\frac{1}{2}$ litre bottles would Hannah need to buy?

   Answer: _____ Marks: ____ /1

2. How many $\frac{1}{4}$ litre bottles would she need to buy?

   Answer: _____ Marks: ____ /1

3. Which option should Hannah buy to get the cheapest deal on water?

   Answer: _____ Marks: ____ /3

4. If Hannah's mum wanted 2 litres of water, how many $\frac{1}{4}$ litres should Hannah buy?

   Answer: _____ Marks: ____ /2

## Super Sleuth challenge 💬

In Ireland, sun cream is often sold in $\frac{1}{4}$ litre bottles. In Australia, it is often sold in 1 litre containers. Why do you think 1 litre containers of sun cream are **not** sold in Ireland?

Today's Marks: ____ /7

113

## **Day Three** Try these.

**1** Nicola's mum is buying handwash for the bathroom. Tick the capacity of the bottle of handwash that you would expect her to buy. Explain your answer to a partner.

> **Top Tip!**
> Simplify.

**(a)** $\frac{1}{4}$ litre ☐        **(b)** 1 litre ☐        **(c)** 2 litres ☐

**Marks:** ☐ /1

**2** Ciarán is making an ice-cream smoothie. He blends together $\frac{1}{4}$ litre of milk, $\frac{1}{2}$ litre of pineapple juice and $\frac{1}{4}$ litre of vanilla ice-cream.

**(a)** What is the total amount of liquid in the smoothie? **(b)** If one serving of smoothie is $\frac{1}{4}$ litre, how many people can Ciarán share his smoothie between?

**Answers: (a)** _____ **(b)** _____ **Marks:** ☐ /2

**3** Joan is shopping for milk. She has 2 children. Each of her children pours $\frac{1}{4}$ litre of milk on their breakfast cereal every morning. The family also drink $\frac{1}{2}$ litre of milk every day. Joan wants to buy enough milk for 3 days.

**(a)** How much milk should she buy?

**(b)** If the milk costs **65c** for 1 litre, how much will Joan pay in total for the milk that she needs to buy?

**Answers: (a)** _____ **(b)** _____ **Marks:** ☐ /4

**Today's Marks:** ☐ /7

## Day Four  Try these.

**CLUES**

**1** In Cathal's fridge there was a 1 litre orange juice carton that was exactly **half full**. He poured half of what was in the carton into his glass. How much orange juice did he pour into his glass?

Answer: ☐ Marks: ☐ /1

**2** Gillian always drinks a $\frac{1}{4}$ litre carton of chocolate milk after hockey training. She has hockey training **3 times a week**. How many quarters of a litre of chocolate milk does she drink in **two weeks**?

Answer: ☐ Marks: ☐ /2

**3** Niall's mum is making up diluted orange for his birthday party. She has a 1 litre bottle of squash. She pours $\frac{1}{4}$ litre of squash into a jug and adds 1 litre of water. This will be enough diluted orange for 5 children, but she needs to make enough for 15 children.

**Team Talk**

Reader
Calculator
Checker
Reporter

**(a)** How many jugs of diluted orange will she need to make up?

**(b)** How much squash will she use?

**(c)** How much water will she use?

Answers: (a) ☐ (b) ☐ (c) ☐ Marks: ☐ /3

Today's Marks: ☐ /6

Total Marks: ☐ /25   Got this! 👍⚪ Getting there. ✋⚪ Need help! ☝⚪

I would like to get better at ☐

# 28 Area

**We are learning to:** Estimate and measure area using non-standard units. ☐

## Day One Look at the example below.

Sally wrote a long letter to her cousin in England, telling him a lot of news. Which size paper do you think she used?

**C**ircle the numbers and keywords:
long letter, a lot of news, which size?

**L**ink with operation needed (+ or −): None

**U**se a strategy: Act it out.

**E**stimate and calculate:
The bigger the sheet of paper, the more the Sally could write.

**Answer:**
the large sheet of writing paper

**S**ummarise how you got your answer:
Sally had a lot to write, so she needed the largest size.

### Keyword

**Area** is the amount of space taken up by a surface.

## Try these.

1) Colm, his younger brother and his dad are making handprints on an A4 sheet of paper. Will the three handprints cover **more than** or **less than half** of the sheet of paper?

Answer: _____ Marks: ☐ /1

2) Michelle was at the zoo and she saw sets of muddy hoof prints. She counted **16** giraffe hooves, **8** camel hooves and **4** elephant hooves. Which of these do you think covered the biggest area?

Answer: _____ Marks: ☐ /1

3) Jess is sticking buttons onto the soles of shoes for an art competition. If she uses **10** buttons to cover the sole of one shoe, how many buttons will she use to cover the soles of **3 pairs** of the same size shoes?

Answer: _____ Marks: ☐ /2

Today's Marks: ☐ /4

**Day Two** Try these.

1. Owen worked out that **10** maths books exactly covered the surface of his rectangular desk. Then he saw that **9** playing cards exactly covered the surface of his maths book. How many playing cards would cover his desk?

Answer: [ ] Marks: [ ] /1

2. Which of these shapes is the odd one out? Explain your answer to a partner.

A

B

C

D

Answer: [                    ] Marks: [ ] /2

3. A baker is icing cakes. **3** cupcakes can be iced from the same amount of icing that it takes to cover the top of **1** birthday cake. How many cupcakes could be iced from the same amount of icing that it takes to cover **3** birthday cakes?

Answer: [              ] Marks: [ ] /2

**Super Sleuth challenge**

Number these scraps of wrapping paper in order starting with the largest area.

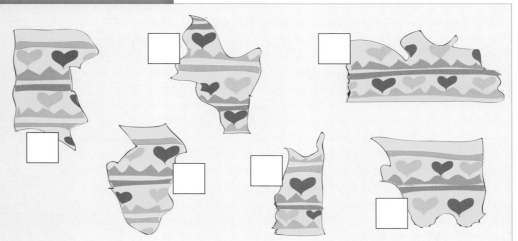

Today's Marks: [ ] /5

117

**Day Three** Try these.

1. Order these items from the one with the largest area of glass to the one with the smallest area of glass.

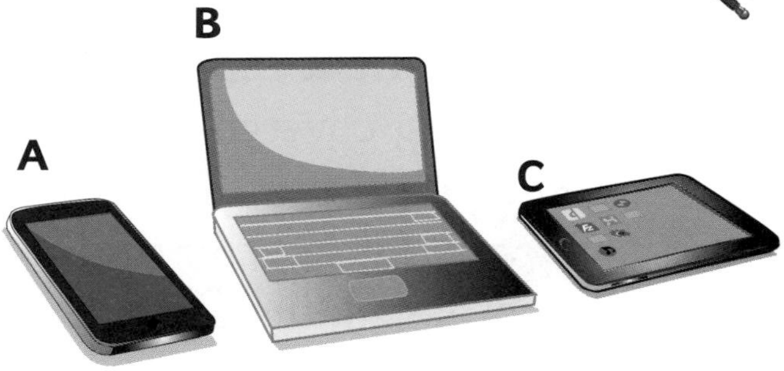

A   B   C

Answer: _____ Marks: ___ /1

2. Five pictures cover the area of **1** display board in Taylor's classroom. How many pictures of the same size would cover **3** display boards?

Answer: ___ Marks: ___ /2

3. Alice the chef can fit **4** steaks on the frying pan at one time. If she fried **16** steaks altogether, how many times did she use the frying pan?

Answer: _____ Marks: ___ /2

4. Wayne's dad wants to buy a new glass door for the kitchen. He knows that one small window is **half** the price of one large window and two large windows are the same price as one door. If one small window costs **€50**, how much does one door cost?

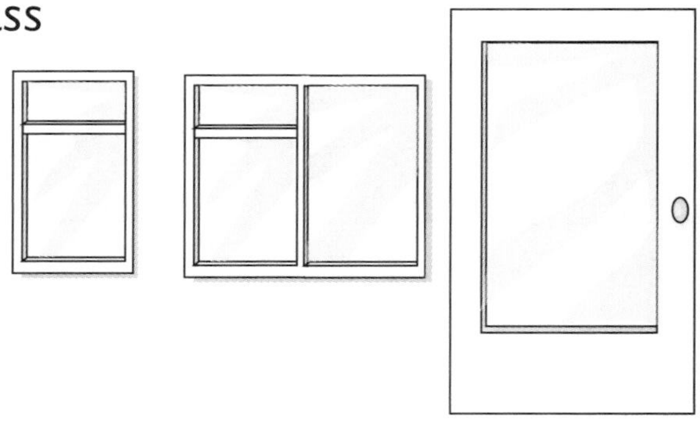

Answer: _____ Marks: ___ /2

Today's Marks: ___ /7

**Day Four** Try these.

① **Five** sheets of wallpaper are used to cover the area of one wall in a square bedroom. How many **more** sheets will be needed to cover the other walls?

Answer: Marks: /1

② At home time in school, the pupils place their chairs on top of their tables so that the floor can be cleaned. If **2** chairs fit on each table, how many tables are needed for **30** chairs?

Answer: Marks: /2

③ During maths class, three pupils each covered a postcard with shapes as follows:

**(a)** Adam covered his postcard with **5** triangles.

**(b)** Lily covered her postcard with **4** circles.

**(c)** Troy covered his postcard with **8** semi-circles.

If each pupil had to cover two more postcards, **how many more** shapes would they need?

Answers: (a) (b) (c) Marks: /3

**Super Sleuth investigates**

Today's Marks: /6

Use your hands and feet to measure the surface area of different items in your classroom or home.

Total Marks: /22 Got this!  Getting there.  Need help!

I enjoyed

# 29 Addition and Subtraction

**We are learning to:** Add numbers, without and with renaming, within 99. ☐
Subtract numbers, without and with renaming, within 99. ☐

## Day One Look at the example below.

Noah's parents bought him a soccer game costing €49 and a soccer ball costing €25 for his birthday. How much did they spend in total?

**C**ircle the numbers and keywords:
€49, €25, how much in total

**L**ink with operation needed (+ or –): Add (+).

**U**se a strategy: Draw a picture.

**E**stimate and calculate:
My estimate: close to €80

$$\begin{array}{r} €4\ 9 \\ +\ €2_15 \\ \hline €7\ 4 \end{array}$$

**Answer:** €74

**S**ummarise how you got your answer:
I added €49 and €25 and got a total of €74.

**Top Tip!**
Round the prices when estimating:
€49 rounds to **€50**.
€25 rounds to **€30**.
**€50 + €30 = €80**

### Try these.

1. Kayley had **€63** in her savings account. The following week, she put **€25** into her account. How much money was in her account then?

   Answer: ☐
   Marks: ☐ /1

2. One day, a toyshop sold **28** scooters in the morning and **36** scooters in the afternoon. How many scooters were sold that day?

   Answer: ☐   Marks: ☐ /1

3. A carpenter had a shelf measuring **98 cm** in length. He sawed off a **13 cm** piece. What length was the shelf then?

   Answer: ☐   Marks: ☐ /1

Today's Marks: ☐ /3

**Day Two** Try these.

**C**LUE**s**

**1** Enrico's dad is buying coal. Each bag of coal costs **€23**. If he buys **3** bags of coal, how much will he pay in total?

**Top Tip!**
Identify a pattern.

Answer: €          Marks:     /1

**2** Nassar's mum's mobile phone bills cost **€22** in November, **€29** in December and **€34** in January. How much did her mobile phone bills cost in total for these winter months?

Answer: €          Marks:     /1

**3** Adam owns a fruit stall. He sells **red** apples in **packs of 6** and **green** apples in **packs of 4**. On Friday, he sold the following:

|  | **Packs of red apples sold** | **Packs of green apples sold** |
|---|---|---|
| Morning | | |
| Afternoon | | |
| Evening | | |

How many **(a) red** apples and **(b) green** apples did he sell in total?
**(c)** How many **fewer green** apples than **red** apples did he sell?

Answers: (a)          (b)          (c)          Marks:     /9

Today's Marks:     /11

121

## Day Three  Try these.

**1** Niall works in a bicycle repair shop. One morning, he counted **47** bicycles in the shop. Only **29** of them had been repaired. How many bicycles still needed to be repaired?

Answer: ____   Marks: ____ /1

**2** One Sunday morning, there were **63** families at the Pebble Beach Holiday Resort. In the afternoon, **24** families went home. In the evening, **13** new families arrived. How many families were at the resort that Sunday evening?

Answer: ____   Marks: ____ /2

**3** One Saturday, Cinema World showed *The BFG* at 2:00, 4:00 and 6:00. The following table shows the number of children and adults who went to see *The BFG* at each of these times:

|  | 2:00 | 4:00 | 6:00 |
| --- | --- | --- | --- |
| Number of children | 26 | 42 | 29 |
| Number of adults | 19 | 37 | 18 |

**(a)** How many children went to see the film that day? **(b)** How many adults went to see the film that day? **(c)** How many fewer adults than children went to see the film that day?

Answers: (a) ____   (b) ____   (c) ____   Marks: ____ /3

Today's Marks: ____ /6

## Day Four  Try these.

**CLUEs**

**1** A bin lorry collected **45** green bins and **38** brown bins in a housing estate. How many bins were collected altogether?

Answer: ___ Marks: ___ /1

**2** Darren had **82** e-books on his e-reader, but he deleted **28** to make space. He downloaded **19** new e-books over the months that followed. How many e-books did he have then?

Answer: ___ Marks: ___ /2

**3** One morning, a hurley maker had **23** hurleys in his workshop. He **sold 9** that morning. He **made 38** more in the afternoon and **sold 17** that evening. How many hurleys did he have left at the end of the day?

Answer: ___ Marks: ___ /3

Today's Marks: ___ /6

## Puzzle power

Oh no, Sum-Bot has broken down! Can you complete each number track for him by adding the two previous numbers?

| 1 | 3 | 4 | 7 | 11 |
|---|---|---|---|---|
| 10 | 12 | | | |
| 20 | 10 | | | |
| 16 | 9 | | | |

Total Marks: ___ /26

Got this!  ○  Getting there. ○ ○  Need help!  ○

My favourite activity was ___

# 30 Revision 5

## Brilliant Birthdays!

**Day One** Try these.

1. How many cones can you count on this castle birthday cake?

Answer: [ ]    Marks: [ ] /1

2. Jonathan got a box of building blocks for his birthday. He took out a number of blocks and counted **16** corners altogether. What kinds of 3-D shapes might they have been?

Answer: [ ]    Marks: [ ] /1

3. Jessie got **3** cuboid-shaped presents for her birthday. How many edges did they have altogether?

Answer: [ ]    Marks: [ ] /2

4. In Max and Leah's classroom, there was a box containing lots of each kind of 3-D shape. Max took a cuboid, a cylinder, a cone and a sphere from the box. Leah took out four 3-D shapes as well, but she did **not** take out any cylinders or cuboids. Leah discovered that her shapes had the same total number of faces and curved surfaces as Max's shapes. What 3-D shapes might Leah have taken out?

Answer: [ ]    Marks: [ ] /4

**Strand:** Shape and Space **Strand Unit:** 3-D Shapes **Strand:** Measures **Strand Units:** Capacity; Area **Strand:** Number **Strand Unit:** Operations – addition and subtraction

**Today's Marks:** [ ] /8

## **Day Two** Try these.

**C**LUE's

**1** Laura's grandad gave her a new flask for her birthday and took her hiking. Laura brought along $\frac{1}{2}$ litre of soup in her flask. If she gave $\frac{1}{4}$ litre to her grandad, how much soup did she have left for herself?

Answer: ___ Marks: ___ /1

**2** Kelly's dad made diluted orange for her birthday party. He used $\frac{1}{4}$ litre of squash to make each jug of diluted orange. If he used $1\frac{1}{2}$ litres of squash in total, how many jugs of diluted orange did he make?

Answer: ___ Marks: ___ /2

**3** For Shane's birthday party, his mum bought a 1 litre carton of pouring custard to make trifles. If she needed $\frac{1}{4}$ litre of custard to make 2 trifles, how many trifles could she make from 1 litre of custard?

**Top Tip!**
Make a table.

Answer: ___ Marks: ___ /2

**4** Keith was planning a birthday lunch for his granny. He knew that he needed $\frac{1}{4}$ litre of cream to make enough soup for 3 people and $\frac{1}{2}$ litre of cream to make enough cheesecake for 3 people. How much cream did he need to make enough soup and cheesecake for **12** people?

Answer: ___ Marks: ___ /3

Today's Marks: ___ /8

125

**Day Three** Try these.

1. Twins Lisa and Sophie share a small bedroom with only enough floor space for 1 single bed. Which of the following should their parents buy for their birthday?

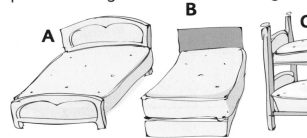

A    B    C

Answer: 
Marks: /1

2. At the bowling alley, Daisy makes hot chocolate for children's parties. If she needs **5** marshmallows to cover the surface of one mug of hot chocolate, how many marshmallows does she need to cover the surface of **2** mugs of hot chocolate?

Answer:     Marks: /1

3. Philip and his family cycled to a pizza restaurant on Philip's birthday. Outside the restaurant, **10** bicycles could fit in **1** car parking space. How many bicycles could fit in **4** car parking spaces?

Answer:     Marks: /1

4. On Abdul's birthday, his mum cooked pancakes for a special breakfast. She was able to fit **4** small pancakes on the frying pan. If she cooked **20** small pancakes, how many times did she use the frying pan?

Answer:     Marks: /2

Today's Marks: /5

## Day Four  Try these.

**CLUEs**

**1** Lots of children went to the seaside for their birthday last summer. One day, Sandy's Seaside Shop sold **36** red, **25** blue and **16** green bucket-and-spade sets. How many sets were sold altogether?

Answer: ☐ Marks: ☐ /1

**2** There were were **56** children at an indoor play centre. **18** children were playing on the climbing frame and **19** were playing in the tunnels. The rest of the children were eating birthday cake. How many children were eating birthday cake?

Answer: ☐ Marks: ☐ /2

**3** Keegan was on a train travelling to his cousin's birthday party. He counted **42** passengers in his carriage. At the next stop, **16** got out and **28** got on. How many passengers were there in Keegan's carriage then?

Answer: ☐ Marks: ☐ /2

Today's Marks: ☐ /5

## Super Sleuth challenge

**Write a number between 1 and 50:**

| Spell it: | Add 3: | | Double it: | |
|---|---|---|---|---|
| | Add 8: | | Halve it: | |
| Is it < or > 32? | Subtract 10: | | Number before: | |
| | Add 10: | | Number after: | |

Total Marks: ☐ /26